# Fly
# Pushing

# Fly Pushing

## The Theory and Practice of *Drosophila* Genetics

### RALPH J. GREENSPAN

New York University

 **Cold Spring Harbor Laboratory Press 1997**

**Acknowledgments**

This book has benefited from the comments and criticisms of many people, to whom I am enormously grateful: Michael Ashburner, Eric Wieschaus, Barry Ganetzky, Steve Small, Angus Wilson, Tim Karr, Nanci Kane, and Sue Broughton. I thank Alison Stewart for her editorial expertise and input, Gerry Rubin for suggesting the idea in the first place, and John Inglis for demonstrating the patience of Job as it was brought to fruition. Above all, I thank Jeff Hall, who first introduced me to the fly and taught me virtually all I know about its genetics.

# Fly Pushing

The Theory and Practice
of *Drosophila* Genetics

© 1997 Cold Spring Harbor Laboratory Press
All rights reserved
Design by Emily Harste

Illustrations on the cover and page x are from Lindsley and Zimm 1992, used and/or modified with permission of the publisher, Academic Press.

Library of Congress Cataloging in Publication Data

Greenspan, Ralph J.
    Fly pushing : the theory and practice of Drosophila genetics /
Ralph J. Greenspan.
        p.   cm.
    Includes bibliographical references (p.  ) and index.
    ISBN 0-87969-492-0
    1. Drosophila—Genetics.   I. Title.
QH470.D7G74  1996
595.77'4—dc20                      96-44171
                                        CIP

All Cold Spring Harbor Laboratory Press publications may be ordered directly from Cold Spring Harbor Laboratory Press, 10 Skyline Drive, Plainview, New York 11803-2500. Phone: 1-800-843-4388 in Continental U.S. and Canada. All other locations: (516) 349-1930. FAX: (516) 349-1946. E-mail: cshpress@cshl.org. For a complete catalog of all Cold Spring Harbor Laboratory Press publications, visit our World Wide Web Site http://www.cshl.org/

# Contents

## CHAPTER 3
# Mapping    47

## CHAPTER 4
# Synthesizing Specific Genotypes    63

# CHAPTER 5
# Analysis of Mutations: I. Characteristics of the Allele                                                    87

# CHAPTER 6
# Analysis of Mutations: II. Mosaics                                                    103

# Fly
# Pushing

## FREQUENTLY USED MARKERS

heterozygous ♀    hemizygous ♂

**Bar (B)** *X*
eye narrower than usual oval shape

**forked (f)** *X*
bristles short with split or bent ends

**singed (sn)** *X*
bristles short, gnarled and wavy

**Scutoid (Sco)** *2nd*
missing bristles especially
from posterior thorax

**Curly (Cy)** *2nd*
wings curled upward instead of flat

**Serrate (Ser)** *3rd*
(also called Beaded–Serrate, *Bd^S*)
wings notched

**Dichaete (D)** *3rd*
wings extended like jet plane
instead of straight back

**Stubble (Sb)** *3rd*
bristles short and stubby

*+/+*          *Ubx/+*

**Ultrabithorax (Ubx)** *3rd*
haltere larger and rounder than normal

**eyeless-Dominant (ey^D)** *4th*
very small eyes

# Introduction

With each passing year, more and more scientists are attracted to work with *Drosophila*, lured by the potential for combining genetic and molecular approaches to questions of gene expression, cell biology, development, and neurobiology. They are aware that there is a large folklore of classical genetic tools lurking somewhere in the fly field—they have seen the results in some of the dazzling findings that have been made—but access to these tools somehow seems to be limited. At times, it may even appear that the wielders of "hard-core" fly genetics preside over a coven with secret rites of initiation. The situation has led many to bemoan the fact that there is not a simple and rational way to gain access to Drosophilid mysteries.

Recent publication of a compendium of facts and commentaries on *Drosophila* genetics and biology by Michael Ashburner (1989) has provided fly workers with a comprehensive reference source for all of the folklore (and much more). Still lacking, however, is a bridge to that folklore for the uninitiated; thus, once again the cries have gone up.

This book attempts to provide that bridge. It is designed for those graduate students, postdocs, and even lab heads who want to use fly genetics in their work. An elementary knowledge of genetics (e.g., undergraduate course level) is assumed, but not much more. The approach used in this book has been worked out over the years in lectures given as part of intensive short-term courses at Cold Spring Harbor Laboratory and the University of California at San Francisco, and in my own laboratory. It owes a major debt to the pedagogical tradition of the late Larry Sandler, as modified and transmitted by his student (my mentor) Jeff Hall.

Each subject is addressed from a practical standpoint, with a bit of the theoretical foundations (such as they are) included to make it intelligible. Although the book does not attempt to be comprehensive, references are made to more complete treatments of particular topics elsewhere (such as the aforementioned talmudic commentaries of Ashburner). Illustrations of each kind of technique are taken from the literature, and practice problems are provided. Although the working out of problems is helpful in learning the principles, it must be borne in mind that there is no substitute for the actual doing of genetic experiments and crosses— "fly pushing," as it is affectionately known.

# CHAPTER 1

# The Basics of Doing a Cross

During the past 85 years, fly genetics has been developed to a high art. Some of this is the result of time and accumulated information, but much of it is due to the construction of several unique genetic "tools," plus a few intrinsic features of fly biology. The net effect is to make mating schemes more reliable and unambiguous by controlling the randomizing and shuffling effect of recombination in meiosis, and to make the physical location of genes on chromosomes easier to determine. The following sections set out some of the basics of fly genetics and looking after fly cultures, as well as a beginner's Rosetta stone of fly nomenclature.

## FLY CHROMOSOMES

Flies have four pairs of chromosomes, usually represented as lines and circles for arms and centromeres:

**Female**

**Male**

"L" refers to the left arm and "R" to the right. The $X$ and fourth chromosomes have major left arms and tiny right arms (standardly drawn with no right arm). The sizes of the $X$, $2L$, $2R$, $3L$, and $3R$ are roughly comparable, whereas chromosome 4 is only about 1/5 as large.

Sex determination in *Drosophila* is based on the ratio of $X$ chromosomes to autosomal sets. In males, one $X$ with two autosomal sets gives a ratio of 0.5, whereas females have a ratio of 1.0. The $Y$ chromosome contains few genes and is not required for most aspects of male development, only for proper sperm motility.

An important feature of fly genetics is the total absence of recombination in males. Whereas recombination is usually lower in the heterogametic sex of a species (the sex with two different sex chromosomes, usually the males), in *Drosophila melanogaster* it is effectively zero. Recombination in females, on the other hand, is alive and well. Its control is achieved by the use of the fly pusher's most distinctive tool: balancer chromosomes. These are chromosomes whose normal gross sequence is so scrambled, as the result of multiple breaks and rejoinings induced by radiation, that they are no longer capable of pairing or recombining with their normal homolog during meiotic prophase. In addition, their presence in a fly is easily recognizable by a dominant marker mutation, and they contain recessive markers as well. Consequently, their transmission to progeny can be tracked unambiguously and, since they effectively block any recombination with their homologs, the transmission of the homolog to progeny can also be tracked unambiguously. This holds true even if the homolog has no dominant marker, due to the fact that homologs segregate reliably. Thus, if the progeny did not get the balancer, it must have gotten the homolog. This is the single most important principle in fly mating schemes.

Balancers, which are discussed in more detail later in this chapter, are a special case of the more common kind of chromosome rearrangement known as inversions. Other rearrangements that will appear in the course of our discussions are translocations, compound chromosomes, deficiencies, and duplications. The major categories of rearrangements with their representations are listed below.

- Inversions, in which two breakage and repair events have occurred in the same chromosome, resulting in an inverted segment (the breakpoints are symbolized by parentheses):

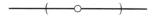

- Translocations, in which breakage events have occurred in two different chromosomes and have been repaired so that the pieces are swapped:

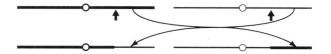

- Compound chromosomes, in which two left or two right arms have become attached to the same centromere (i.e., attached-*X*, attached-*2L*,
  attached-*4*):

- Deficiencies (also called deletions), in which two breaks have occurred in
  the same chromosome and the repair event has excluded the excised
  piece:

- Duplications, in which an excised piece is inserted into another
  chromosome:

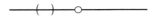

Another important intrinsic feature of the fly is the presence of polytene
chromosomes in the salivary glands. These have distinctive, high-resolution
banding patterns. Early on, they made it possible to correlate map positions
of genes with physical features of the chromosome and to determine the
breakpoint locations of chromosome rearrangements. In the molecular era,
they have facilitated the mapping of cloned DNA sequences to physical
locations (Fig. 1, top). Each of the major chromosome arms is divided into
20 numbered segments, 1–20 for the *X*, 21–40 for *2L*, 41–60 for *2R*, 61–80
for *3L*, and 81–100 for *3R* (Fig. 1, bottom). Chromosome *4* is divided into
regions 101–104. Each numbered region is then divided into lettered
regions (A,B,C,D,E), and each lettered region into numbered bands. (The
number of lettered regions and numbered bands for each numbered region
is not constant along the chromosome, but depends on local topography.)

## RECOGNIZING MARKERS

Marker mutations are the key to deciphering genotypes. Sometimes they
are used to mark the chromosomes you are specifically trying to follow, but
more often they mark the chromosome you are trying to lose. In any event,
a vast array of mutations affecting eye color, eye shape, wing shape, wing
vein morphology, bristle color, bristle shape, and cuticle pigmentation—just
to name the major categories—serve to tag the various chromosome arms.

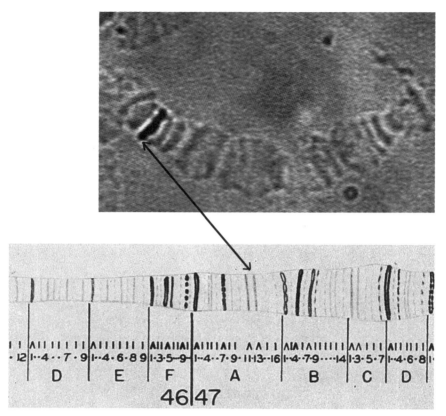

**Figure 1** In situ hybridization to larval polytene chromosome. (*Top*) Enzymatically stained DNA hybridized to band 47A11-14 region (courtesy of P. Tolias). (*Bottom*) Bridges' original drawing of the same chromosome region.

Descriptions of mutant phenotypes can be found in Lindsley and Zimm (1992), for those preferring the printed page, and on FlyBase for the cybernetically inclined (see Appendix). Some of the most commonly used markers are shown on p. x. One simply gets used to recognizing them. The important points to bear in mind about markers concern their consistency of expression and their interactions with each other.

Consistency of expression is reflected in the likelihood that a fly of mutant genotype will show a mutant phenotype (penetrance) and if it does, how much of a range those phenotypes will span (expressivity). The "rank" assigned to mutations in Lindsley and Zimm embodies these parameters, with the highest (RK1) showing the greatest consistency. When selecting positively for a given marker, a certain amount of inconsistency can be tolerated. The worst that will happen is that a few flies will be missed. Much more dangerous, however, is selecting against a particular marker (i.e., saving flies based on the absence of the marker). In these cases, it is crucial to be able to rely on the marker's consistency of expression—or at least to be aware of any possible inconsistency. The RK rating helps discern which markers are problematic until you get a feel for it.

Interactions between markers become important as soon as you find yourself in the situation of using two that affect the same trait. For instance, when using two different mutations affecting bristle shape, it is crucial to know what the double mutant looks like and whether it is distinguishable from each single mutant. Rarely can this information be found in Lindsley and Zimm (except for certain eye-color mutations). Instead, one often has to proceed empirically.

## NOMENCLATURE

*Fly nomenclature is a paper tiger.*
from the uncollected sayings
of Mao Zedong

The shorthand of *Drosophila* genetics can be reduced to a few simple rules, illustrated in the examples that follow (see also FlyBase).

1. $f$; $cn$ $bw$; $\dfrac{TM2}{tra}$

   This example demonstrates several points:

   - The genotype of a chromosome is indicated only if there is a mutation or some other kind of variant on it, and chromosomes are always listed in the order: $X/Y$; 2; 3; 4. In this example: $f$; $cn$ $bw$; $TM2/tra$ refer to the $X$; second; and third chromosomes, respectively.
   - Fly genotypes (e.g., $f$) are always italicized; mutant names (e.g., forked) when written out are traditionally not italicized, although some journals do italicize them nowadays. This book follows the traditional convention.
   - Mutant names are abbreviated with three letters or fewer (although this rule has been abandoned in recent years because there are so many mutants to name (e.g., *norpA* and *disco*); $f$ denotes forked affecting bristle morphology; $cn$ is for cinnabar, and $bw$ is for brown, both affecting eye color such that together they produce a white eye;

TM2 indicates the balancer chromosome "third multiple #2"; and *tra* denotes transformer, a gene required for sex determination.

- Lowercase abbreviations indicate recessive phenotypes, uppercase indicate dominants, locus names taken from enzyme or protein names (e.g., *Adh* for the structural gene for alcohol dehydrogenase) or, as in this case, a particular chromosome rearrangement (the balancer chromosome *TM2*).
- Semi-colons separate the genotype symbols for different chromosomes; in the example above, genotypes of the *X*; second; and third chromosomes are indicated.
- Commas follow the name of a rearrangement and indicate mutations on that chromosome (e.g., the full name of *TM2* is *TM2, Ubx$^{130}$* because it carries a mutant allele of Ultrabithorax known as number *130*).
- A chromosomal genotype written on a single line indicates that the stock is homozygous for that genotype; heterozygosity is denoted by a two-line genotype (as in *TM2/tra* above), each line corresponding to one of the homologs present (note that in publications, the genotype is denoted as *TM2/tra*, all on one line as done here).
- Anything that is not shown is presumed to be wild type; thus, *f* means that the *X* chromosome carries a mutant allele of forked; all other *X*-chromosome loci are presumed to be wild type; similarly when heterozygosity is indicated, only the mutant loci (or rearrangements) are shown for each chromosome.

2.  $\dfrac{C(1)RM,\, y^2}{Y}$ ; $\dfrac{In(2LR)O,\, Cy}{Sco}$ ; $\dfrac{ci^D}{ey^D}$

- *C(1)RM* denotes a compound chromosome. *C(1)* shows that it is a compound of the first chromosome, and *RM* refers to the fact that it is reversed metacentric, i.e., the centromere is in the middle (metacentric) and in the linear order of the chromosome, one arm is reversed relative to the other (i.e., both are attached at the same end); a common shorthand for *C(1)* is $\widehat{XX}$, attached-*X*.
- This particular attached-*X* is homozygous for the *y$^2$* allele (the second one ever found) for the gene affecting cuticle color: yellow; it has black bristles and yellow cuticle, which differs from the first yellow (*y*) by the fact that its bristles are yellow as well as its cuticle.
- Since the attached-*X* contains both homologs of the *X* on one centromere, they do not segregate from each other. Usually these stocks are kept such that both males and females carry a *Y*; this is to

ensure that all of the males will be fertile. (The presence of a *Y* chromosome has nothing to do with sex determination and has no effect on females with two *X*s, but it is essential for sperm motility. Since the *Y* segregates from the *X* in males, the only way their sons can receive a *Y* is if they obtain it from their mothers, a result of its segregation from the attached-*X*. By having a *Y* present in all flies of the stock, this will occur reliably.)

- The genotype of the second chromosome in this stock is heterozygosity for two different chromosomes: One is a balancer known as *In(2LR)O,Cy* (sometimes referred to colloquially and variously as "Curly-O," *CyO*, "Curly-Oster," or "Curly of Oster," named after Irwin Oster who produced it), which carries the dominant mutation *Cy* causing wing-curling, and the other is a chromosome with the dominant mutation Scutoid (*Sco*) which eliminates certain thoracic bristles; the *In(2LR)* refers to the multiple inversions (*In*) involving the left (*L*) and right (*R*) arms of the second (2) chromosome.

- The final chromosome genotype refers to the fourth chromosome, which is heterozygous for two dominant alleles of genes for which most other alleles are recessive, eyeless and cubitus interruptus. This represents an exception to the convention of capital letters for dominant mutations, instead using the superscripted $D$ to indicate dominance of these alleles. Since both of these alleles are homozygous lethal, all flies will be heterozygous for both (this apparent exception to the naming convention follows the rule that loci originally defined by recessive mutations, such as *ey*, will continue to be designated by small letters even after dominant alleles are found).

- Chromosome rearrangements are designated by an abbreviated symbol followed by the chromosome affected (*1, 2, 3,* or *4*) and the name of the rearrangement. For example:

$In(1)sc^4$  inversion on the *X* chromosome called "*scute-4*" and producing a mutant phenotype because of a break in the *scute* locus (breakpoints are symbolized by parentheses);

*Df(3R)P14*  a deletion (deficiency) of part of the right arm of the third chromosome (3R) whose name, *P14*, stands for Pasadena-14;

3L                                             3R

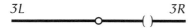

*T(1;4)B^s*    translocation between the first and fourth chromosomes, in which there is a break in each and a reciprocal rejoining, producing a severe Bar eye phenotype called Bar of Stone (*B^s*);

instead of

*X*                4

*Tp(3;1)ry^{35}*    transposition (*Tp*) of a piece of the third chromosome into the *X*, one of whose breakpoints produces a mutant phenotype in the eye-color gene rosy; sometimes designated as translocation *T(3;1)ry^{35}*; transpositions can also refer to the movement of a segment from one place to another in the same chromosome; when this *X* is present in a strain whose third chromosomes are both normal, it becomes a "duplication," designated *Dp(3;1)ry^{35}*;

*X*                              3

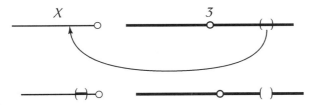

*R(1)w^{vC}*    ring-*X*, an *X* chromosome with no free ends, this particular one has abnormal expression (variegation, hence the "*v*") of the white gene affecting eye color (the "*C*" refers to Catcheside, its originator);

*C(3L)RM, h*  compound chromosome consisting of two left arms of the third chromosome, also known as "attached-3L," homozygous for the original allele of the mutation hairy (*h*), producing extra hairs on the thorax and head. "*RM*"

stands for reversed metacentric; jargon that means the two left arms of chromosome 3 are attached to the same centromere instead of each one attached to a separate centromere with a right arm. "Metacentric" refers to the fact that the centromere is in the middle and "reversed" refers to the fact that the order of genes from one 3L to the next reverses when passing through the centromere, such that the normal 3L chromosome tips are still at the tips. (This contrasts with a "tandem metacentric" in which the gene order repeats identically when passing through the centromere, and where the tip of one arm is now at the centromere.)

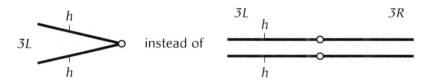

F(2L)          "free" left arm of the second chromosome, in which only a single left arm (2L) is on one centromere.

$y^+Y$          duplication on the Y chromosome of the chromosomal segment carrying a wild-type allele of yellow, also designated as $Tp(1;Y) y^+$;

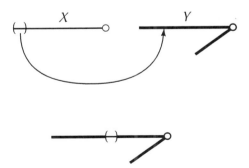

*Note:* Capital Y signifies the chromosome, small y signifies the yellow locus.

## WHAT MAKES FLIES SO GREAT? BALANCER CHROMOSOMES

Balancer chromosomes are what set fly genetics apart from genetics in all other organisms. Most recessive mutations are invisible in heterozygous condition. The ability to carry out crosses such that invisible genotypes can be scored in progeny with virtually 100% reliability has given fly genetics a degree of ease and power unmatched in other diploids.

H.J. Muller invented the idea of balancers, as he did much of the rest of what has become hard-core genetic analysis in the fly (Alfred Sturtevant was responsible for most of the rest), when he first identified the chromosome *C1B* as a suppressor of exchange on the *X* and used it to isolate new *X*-linked lethal mutations (Muller 1918). Since then, the principle has been elaborated that multiply inverted chromosomes are highly unlikely to undergo exchange with their normal homologs. When these chromosomes are also carriers of marker mutations, they become powerful tools in segregation analysis and in the predictable synthesis of defined genotypes. Since the markers are often recessive lethal themselves, the chromosomes provide a means for constructing true-breeding stocks for defined lethal mutations—"balanced lethal" stocks in which only those adults doubly heterozygous for the balancer and for the lethal-bearing homolog survive.

Many balancers exist for the *X*, second, and third chromosomes. They are not necessary for chromosome 4 because there is no exchange on that chromosome. The most effective balancers are those that suppress exchange all along the chromosome. Those that fail to do so usually have a large enough portion in normal order to permit occasional synapsis with a homolog and consequent double cross-overs within the short intervals that succeed in pairing. This can result in "breakdown" of the balancer—replacement of portions by a normal sequence, with transfer of some markers to the normal homolog. These are situations clearly to be avoided, because they confound the usefulness of balancers.

Since the *X* chromosome must exist in hemizygous condition in males, most *X*-chromosome balancers do not contain recessive lethals. Instead, some *X*-chromosome balancers carry recessive female sterile mutations to prevent them from "taking over" the stock (i.e., becoming the only *X* chromosomes present, which will occur if the other chromosome carries mutations that are unhealthier than those on the balancer).

Balancers are usually named with a letter for their chromosome (**F** for first which is the *X*, **S** for second, and **T** for third), with an **M** for multiply inverted and with a number and sometimes a lowercase letter to identify its place in a series. The name is then sometimes followed by the genetic symbol for the principal markers carried by that balancer. As shown below, there can be more than one version of a balancer. The most efficient balancers are as follows:

*For the X chromosome*

- *FM7a* (real name *In(1)FM7, $y^{31d}$ $sc^8$*), which carries the dominant marker Bar (*B*), as well as recessive alleles of yellow (*$y^{31d}$*), scute (*$sc^8$*), white–apricot (*$w^a$*), and vermilion (*$v^{Of}$*).
- *FM7b*, which carries *$y^{31d}$*, *$sc^8$*, *$w^a$*, and a recessive female-sterile allele of lozenge (*$lz^{sp}$*).
- *FM7c*, which carries *$y^{31d}$*, *$sc^8$*, *$w^a$*, and a recessive female-sterile allele of singed (*$sn^{X2}$*) in addition to alleles of vermilion (*$v^{Of}$*) and garnet (*$g^4$*).

*For the second chromosome*

- *SM6* (real name *In(2LR)SM6, $al^2$ Cy $dp^{lvl}$ $cn^2$ $sp^2$*), which carries the dominant marker Curly (*Cy*) as well as various recessives dumpy (*dp*), cinnabar (*cn*), and speck (*sp*).
- *In(2LR)O, Cy $dp^{lvl}$ pr $cn^2$* (sometimes referred to as *CyO* or "Curly of Oster" named for its creator), which carries Curly (*Cy*) and the recessives dumpy (*dp*), purple (*pr*), and cinnabar (*cn*).

*For the third chromosome*

- *TM3* (real name *In(3LR)TM3, $y^+$ ri $p^p$ sep $bx^{34e}$ e*), which carries the wild-type allele of yellow (*$y^+$*) and the recessives radius incompletus (*ri*), pink peach (*$p^p$*), sepia (*sep*), bithorax (*$bx^{34e}$*), and ebony (*e*). More useful are those versions carrying the dominant marker Stubble (*Sb*) or Serrate (*Ser*), also called Beaded-Serrate (*$Bd^S$*).
- *TM6* (real name *In(3LR)TM6, $Hn^P$ $ss^{P88}$ $bx^{34e}$ $Ubx^{P15}$ e*), which carries the dominants Henna (*$Hn^P$*, not so easy to score) and the more reliable Ultrabithorax (*$Ubx^{P15}$*) plus the recessives spineless (*$ss^{P88}$*), bithorax (*$bx^{34e}$*), and ebony (*e*).
- *TM6B* (real name *In(3LR)TM6, Hu e*), which carries a dominant allele of Antennapedia (*Hu*), often with the additional dominants Dichaete (*$D^3$*) or Tubby (*Tb*, a good marker for larval and pupal stages as well) and the recessive ebony (*e*).
- *TM8* (real name *In(3LR)TM8, l(3R)DTS th st Sb e*), which carries a dominant temperature-sensitive lethal (*l(3R)DTS*), the dominant Stubble (*Sb*), and the recessives thread (*th*), scarlet (*st*), and ebony (*e*). *TM9* is a further derivative of this.

- *T(2;3) CyO; TM9*, which is a double balancer for chromosomes 2 and 3, the result of a radiation-induced reciprocal translocation between *In(2LR)O,Cy* and *TM9*. Since it is a reciprocal translocation, in which part of *In(2LR)O,Cy* is now linked to part of *TM9* and the remainders are also linked together, all the pieces must be present in the same gamete in order for it to be euploid (i.e., have a complete haploid genome).

## DECIPHERING MATING SCHEMES

After nomenclature, the next most obfuscated realm of fly lore is the mating scheme. Mating schemes are shorthand for the genotypes needed to be collected and mated to get the desired progeny. One of their confusing aspects is that the schemes do not show all the progeny possible from a cross, only the genotype of the unique desired class. These flies will be unique in phenotype as well as genotype if the author of the scheme has planned correctly. The unwritten assumptions are that homologous chromosomes pair and segregate from each other in the first meiotic division, that all possible combinations of haploid segregants will be produced with equal frequency in the male's sperm and female's eggs, and that likewise all possible combinations of diploid genotypes will be produced with equal frequency when eggs are fertilized. Whether they all survive is a separate matter. Our assumption is that they will be produced initially (with the caveat that some abnormal chromosomes deviate from normal expectations). The shorthand indicates the genotypes of the relevant pairs of homologs for the cross at hand.

A typical, simple scheme is shown below:

$$\male\male \quad \frac{nd}{Y} \quad \times \quad \frac{FM7a}{FM7a'} \cdot \frac{In(2LR)O,Cy}{Sco} \quad \female\female$$

Males    $\downarrow$                 Virgin females

$$\frac{FM7a}{nd} \cdot \frac{In(2LR)O,Cy}{+}$$

This represents a cross between notchoid *(nd)* males (they must be males because they have one *X* and a *Y*, and the fact that it is more than one male is symbolized by $\male\male$), and females (virgins, of course, symbolized by $\female\female$) homozygous for the balancer chromosome *FM7a* on the *X* and heterozygous for the balancer *In(2LR)O,Cy* and the dominant marker Scutoid *(Sco)* on the second chromosome. Since the male's genotype does not show anything about his second or third chromosomes, they are assumed to be free of genetic variations and mutations (+). (In the Methods section of a paper, these balancers would be designated by their formal names: In(1)FM7a and In(2LR)O,Cy. In lab shorthand, they would usually be abbreviated as in most of the examples in this book. As mentioned, some forms of FM7 carry a recessive, female-sterile mutation; FM7a does not and so would work in this cross.)

This cross will produce many different classes of progeny. Only one of them is shown: females heterozygous on the X for FM7a and for nd and heterozygous on the second chromosome for In(2LR)O,Cy. Meanwhile, elsewhere in the bottle you will also find:

$$\frac{FM7a}{Y}; \frac{In(2LR)O,Cy}{+}, \qquad \frac{FM7a}{Y}; \frac{Sco}{+} \quad \text{and} \quad \frac{FM7a}{nd}; \frac{Sco}{+}$$

$$\qquad\qquad \male \qquad\qquad\qquad \male \qquad\qquad\qquad \female$$

each of which is phenotypically, as well as genotypically, unique. The dominant marker on the FM7a chromosome, Bar (B) eye, makes any progeny carrying FM7a unambiguously recognizable. Similarly, on the second chromosome, the dominant marker on In(2LR)O,Cy, the Curly (Cy) wing mutation, and the dominant marker mutation Scutoid (Sco), which eliminates posterior thoracic bristles, make any fly carrying these mutations recognizable in any combination, since they do not mask each other. The nd mutation is effectively invisible. It has no morphological effect when heterozygous (in females). (Bar is particularly well suited as a dominant marker for the X chromosome because it is viable in homozygous as well as heterozygous condition, and the two are distinguishable; B/B females are more severely affected than B/+. In males, there is no homozygosity for the X, only hemizygosity [B/Y in males is as severe as B/B in females], so Bar's viability is very helpful in allowing survival of males carrying FM7a. In contrast, the dominant markers on autosomal balancers never need to survive in hemizygotes because hemizygosity for chromosome 2 or 3 is lethal.)

The unwritten assumption in these schemes is that meiosis causes each pair of homologs to segregate from each other so that only one of each pair is transmitted to any given progeny (Mendel's law of segregation). This occurs independently for each pair of homologs (Mendel's law of independent assortment). The parental males in the cross are hemizygous for their sex chromosomes, nd/Y, and will consequently display the mutant nd phenotype. Since the *X* and *Y* pair and segregate at meiosis, they will give rise to gametes of two possible genotypes: *nd* or *Y*. The parental females, even though they carry balancers and marker mutations for two different chromosomes, are only heterozygous on the second chromosome and will thus give rise to only two possible gametes: *FM7a; In(2LR)O,Cy* or *FM7a; Sco*. These four gametic genotypes can combine in four possible combinations, as shown above. Heterozygosity on any other chromosomes increases the possible types of gametes and the corresponding classes of progeny. If in doubt about the classes of progeny that might arise from a cross, you can always draw out a "Punnett Square" to make sure you are imagining all possible combinations.

female gametes

|  |  | *FM7a; In(2LR)O,Cy* | *FM7a; Sco* |
|---|---|---|---|
| male gametes | *nd* | $\dfrac{FM7a}{nd}; \dfrac{In(2LR)O,Cy}{+}$ | $\dfrac{FM7a}{nd}; \dfrac{Sco}{+}$ |
|  | *Y* | $\dfrac{FM7a}{Y}; \dfrac{In(2LR)O,Cy}{+}$ | $\dfrac{FM7a}{Y}; \dfrac{Sco}{+}$ |

Even better than the Punnett Square is the "algebraic" or branching approach, which is better suited to multiply mutant genotypes:

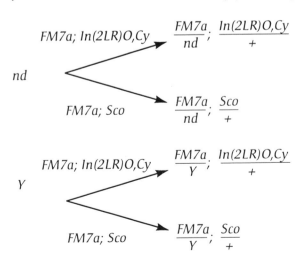

The most important point is to make sure that the genotypic class you want is phenotypically unique and thus recognizable among all the other progeny. This is the key to fly genetics.

## BASIC FLY HUSBANDRY

Fortunately for many of us in the fly field, working with *Drosophila* doesn't take much technical skill. Care, yes; but not manual skill. Much of the power of fly genetics comes from the ability to perform crosses in which each possible genotype in the progeny is recognized easily and unambiguously. In order to achieve this, it is necessary to ensure that the only progeny obtained are from the intended cross, rather than from stray flies or from unwanted pregnancies (i.e., non-virgin females). Often the class of progeny you are trying to generate will be a small fraction of the total and may not be particularly healthy. This means that it is equally important to start the cross with enough flies so that you will recover enough of the progeny needed to continue the experiment.

The easiest way to grow flies is at room temperature. This also protects your stocks from incubator failures—by far the major cause of catastrophic loss among fly workers. The healthiest way to keep fly stocks, on the other hand, is at 25°C, 60% relative humidity. At this temperature, you will get the fastest generation time and the best viability, with a generation time of approximately 9–10 days from egg to emerged adult. (The generation time increases by roughly 2 days if the mold inhibitor Tegosept is present. See Ashburner [1989].) Stocks can also be maintained routinely at temperatures as high as 29°C and as low as 18°C with correspondingly faster or slower generation times (see Ashburner 1989) but with poorer yield.

For stocks that are true breeding (i.e., where all adult progeny are the same genotype), the only time limitation on the life of the culture is that of health; older cultures produce less healthy flies and serve as a breeding ground for mold and mites, the scourge of all stock collections. A good rule of thumb for these cultures is to transfer them every 2 weeks and to keep them a maximum of 18 days at 25°C. Cultures that are produced from a specific cross have an additional constraint: 18 days after the start of the culture, you will begin to obtain second-generation progeny whose genotype will probably be a complete mystery, since you will not have known who the parents were.

True-breeding stocks can be transferred without anesthetization. This technique constitutes one of the only manual skills in fly pushing: Tap the flies down to the bottom of the old vial (gently, so they don't all get stuck in the food at the bottom), quickly take off the vial's plug (usually cotton, rayon, or foam rubber), and then place an open fresh vial down on top of it, holding the two vial mouths together tightly. Flip them over and tap the flies down into the new vial (gently, so as not to transfer the old food as well). Then quickly plug the new vial. For the first few weeks, you will proba-bly have a lot of stray flies escaping. To keep the number of stray flies in the lab to a minimum, it is wise to use some kind of fly trap. Low-tech versions consist of a clean culture bottle with some vinegar in the bottom and a dash of detergent, topped with an open funnel to impede the flies' escape before they fall into the liquid. High-tech fly traps are the commercial "bug lights" familiar to suburban backyards. Screen doors have sometimes been used (S. Hawley, pers. comm.), but they may violate fire regulations.

Since fly stocks can only be maintained by live culturing (they do not readily survive freezing), it is worthwhile to keep duplicates of each stock. It also ensures having cultures available for virgin collection at any time. For stocks kept in vials, which covers most stocks, this can be done by keeping two copies, either on the same schedule or staggered by a half generation. Labeling of stocks is equally important, and most easily accomplished by using a movable ring tag (a cardboard disc attached to the vial by a rubber band) with the full genotype of the stock written on it. The date of initiation of each culture (when flies were first put on that food) should also be writ-ten on the vial or bottle so that you can easily tell their age.

The number of flies needed to start a culture varies with the viability of the genotype, and there is a golden mean for each. A little empiricism goes a long way when it comes to figuring out how many flies to put in a bottle. In general, the more mutants present (especially dominants), the poorer the viability. Chromosome rearrangements (e.g., balancers, compound chromo-somes) reduce the fertility of stocks. Too few flies and the culture will not "take" or will be overwhelmed by mold or bacteria. Too many flies and the culture will become so soggy from the cumulative waste products that when you dump flies from it, the food will come out as well, leaving a dis-gusting mess all over your anesthetizer and fly desk. Soggy cultures have the further problem of causing the flies' wings to stick to their bodies, making it difficult or impossible to score the wing phenotype of many use-ful genetic markers. If a culture looks like it's getting too soggy, you can sometimes rescue it by stuffing a small piece of paper towel into the food. To prevent the paper from growing mold, it too may need to be treated with mold inhibitor.

Wild-type stocks or those with a single marker mutation may require only 10–15 females for a small bottle, 25–35 females for a large bottle, 4–8 for a vial. Fewer males are required, as one male can make himself known to many females. Stocks with multiple markers, dominants, or rearrangements may require two or three times as many flies. The best way to compensate for not knowing exactly how many flies to start with is to watch the culture as it develops. When the food starts to look churned up (especially near the surface), there are enough larvae and it's time to dump out the parents. This can take roughly 4 days, depending on the genotypes. When doing a cross, it is important to dump the parents (empty them from the bottle before the first progeny emerge) for an additional reason: so that there is no danger of mistaking progeny for their parents. This is another good reason for writing the date on the culture when you start it.

## CODDLING DIFFICULT STRAINS

Also known as cosseting (in the U.K.), this refers to the gentle art of keeping sickly stocks, rescuing those that have deteriorated to very few flies, or carrying out crosses with a single male and female pair. The basic principles of sound fly husbandry apply: Use a fresh food vial garnished with fresh yeast paste (baker's dried active yeast mixed to the consistency of peanut butter), keep the culture in ideal conditions (25°C, 60% humidity), and say an occasional prayer.

If you managed to start out with both males and females in the vial (which doesn't always happens with a deteriorating stock) and you find that progeny are appearing, it is best to collect them as they emerge and place them in a fresh vial. They will not live long if left in the original culture vial. In this fashion, you can start a new culture. If you have obtained enough flies for the next culture to go more quickly (i.e., larval churning of the food after several days), you may transfer the parents to a fresh vial midway and thus increase the number of progeny you will ultimately obtain.

## COLLECTING FLIES FOR CROSSES

To carry out crosses cleanly, you must start with virgin females. At 25°C, female flies will not mate within the first 8 hours of emergence as adults. This means that virgins are most easily obtained by collecting flies twice a day—once in the morning and again 7–8 hours later. Morning is when the majority of flies emerge from the pupa case (if your incubator is on a light:dark cycle), as one of their most predominant circadian rhythms (also the origin of the name *Drosophila*, as you may have learned in high school). Although you may not assume that all of the females present in the culture in the morning are virgins, many of them will be newly emerged and thus recognizable by their pale pigmentation and by the presence of a dark spot in their translucent abdomens. (This dark spot is the fly's version of meconium, leftovers in the intestine from their last meal.) If you have been careful about clearing all the adults from the bottle in the morning (including those that have stuck to the side or the food), any females present 7–8 hours later will also be virgins, even if they no longer look newly emerged.

A more efficient method for maximizing the number of virgins present in the morning is to place the cultures at 18°C overnight, after your collection at the end of the day. Development is slowed down sufficiently at this temperature that there is roughly a 98% probability that newly emerged females will not mate for 16 hours. Thus, your morning collections can be assumed to be virgins (if the bottles have been properly cleared at the last collection) and you simply alternate the cultures between 25°C during the day and 18°C at night. The 2% error will not matter if non-virginity is distinguishable among progeny of the cross (see below). If non-virginity is not distinguishable, then the more conservative approach is better.

For many crosses it is possible to control for non-virginity by the use of a "virginity marker"—any recessive marker mutation that is homozygous in the stock from which the females come and which will not be homozygous in the intended cross. If progeny appear that carry this marker, they did not come from virgins and they can be tossed. When you are in the middle of a mating scheme, where you are not starting from homozygous strains, it is still often possible to compensate for non-virginity by anticipating the possible genotypes and marker combinations that would appear if there were some non-virgins in the cross. If you can arrange the scheme so that these will be different from the markers that distinguish the desired progeny, then you are safe.

Males for a cross may be collected at almost any time; the only consideration is that they will mate much more efficiently if they are 3 days old or more at the time they are placed with virgins, and they will not mate efficiently if they are too old (>10–15 days). This is due to a maturation process that males go through after eclosion, making them more likely to court and mate with females. In this sense, females are more mature than males when they emerge as adults. (So what else is new?)

Although the sex ratio is indeed 1:1, it is not necessarily so on each day's collection. Female flies develop faster than males, so there will be more of them in the earlier days of the culture than later.

It is often most convenient to store the flies you have collected before mating them in order to start the cross all at once—perhaps because it takes several days to collect enough flies, or because the food hasn't been made yet, or because you may prefer to start all of your crosses on Fridays. (The virtue of starting crosses on Fridays is that the first progeny will emerge 10 days later, on Monday. Thus, you can collect progeny for 5 days, start a new cross the next Friday, and in this fashion free up the occasional weekend day. But don't tell your advisor where you heard this.) Fresh food vials (i.e., that have not had flies in them) are the best place to store flies, 20–30 flies to a vial. If they are to be kept this way for more than a few days, you will need to change the vials to keep the flies healthy. In uncrowded, fresh vials flies can live for 40–60 days, but their fertility falls off gradually to near zero by this time.

During this storage period, it is also possible to ensure that you have actual virgins by seeing that no larvae begin to churn up the food. Toward the end of the storage period, you can also ensure that the culture will go quickly when you do transfer the flies to bottles by "pre-incubating" males and females a day or so in advance in vials. In this way, many of the females will have mated by the time you put them in bottles. Like any second-order reaction, mating proceeds more quickly in the crowded conditions of a vial where collisions between males and females have a higher probability.

Nowadays, most people use $CO_2$ to anesthetize flies for virgin collection and for examining markers. Various gadgets have been devised for delivering the $CO_2$ through diffusers on a flat surface so that a low level of gas can be kept on while you sort through the flies. (The porous polyethylene that is used to plug the bottoms of chromatography columns is good for this purpose.) Usually, a $CO_2$ hose is first inserted into the bottle or vial to anesthetize the flies, or else they are dumped into an anesthetizer—a porous vessel that exposes the flies to the gas.

The traditional way of anesthetizing flies is with ether. Ether anesthetizers consist of an enclosed container (often an empty fly bottle) with a cotton wad in the bottom into which ether is poured and with a porous tube holding the flies. Care was always needed not to over-anesthetize the flies—something that is much less likely with $CO_2$. Once the flies are anesthestized, it is necessary to do all the sorting before they reawaken, which can happen quickly during the summer's heat.

The principal ill effects of such anesthetization are behavioral. Both $CO_2$ and ether impair neural activity for some time. For this reason, a minimum of 24 hours recovery time is required after anesthetization before any behavioral test.

# CHAPTER 2
# Isolating New Variants

The reason we work with flies is not because they are cute—although Ed Lewis has said that you do have to love your organism. We work with them primarily because of mutations—the potential for getting and analyzing them. Much of today's enormous edifice of molecular manipulation in *Drosophila* has grown up around this central fact.

Most forms of mutagenesis do not permit targeting of the event to a predetermined gene—as in the so-called "knock-out" technique in the mouse (a name as descriptive of the effect on one's thinking as on the gene in question). Instead, they approximate a random process from which lesions in the desired gene are generally obtained by genetic testing of individual mutation-bearing flies for complementation or homozygosity. There are few selection schemes of the sort used with microorganisms that are applicable to flies.

## Principles

Mutagens are not completely random in their action, but they approximate it closely enough for the purposes of designing mutant screens. Generally, you treat male flies with a mutagen, or perform a cross to produce males with mobilized transposable elements, and then "clone" individual treated chromosomes in the F1 generation. This is necessary because after a mutagenesis treatment each sperm is unique. Thus, unless you are able to recognize and recover a newly induced mutation in the next generation, you will be out of luck. Many of the desired mutations are either hard to recognize or to recover. For instance, it is hard to get a lethal mutation out of a dead fly.

Males are most often used because: (1) mature sperm are quite sensitive to mutagens, (2) the flies are still capable of performing their conjugal duties after the treatment, and (3) one male will mate with many females to propagate the treated chromosomes. Treatment of females creates problems due to the deleterious effects of mutagens on the oocyte itself and the tendency of the oocyte to soak up mutagen, thereby decreasing its effective concentration in the nucleus. There are instances, however, in which females are the only choice because the mutagenic event requires the presence of both homologs and therefore must occur in a cell whose chromosomes have not yet completed the first meiotic segregation. The induction of compound chromosomes, whose homologous arms are attached to the same centromere, is an example.

Most, but not all, individual F1 flies carry a mutagenized set of chromosomes in all of their germ cells. Since chemical mutagens often act on a single strand of the DNA double helix, F1 progeny will potentially be mosaic for the lesion as a result of the semi-conservative replication of that chromosome. That is, alteration of the sequence on one strand of the DNA by the mutagen will be transmitted to one of the two daughter cells at the first mitosis. As a result, a new mutation will be present in some cells of the animal but not others. This could produce a mutant phenotype without being transmissible if it is present in the tissues crucial to the phenotype but not in the germ cells. The chance that the germ cells in one F1 individual will be mosaic is, however, low. This means that the screen should be designed so that F1 flies will be test-crossed in such a way as to reveal the presence of new mutations in one class of progeny, while allowing recovery of the mutation-bearing chromosome in sibling progeny (see below).

## MUTAGENS

The kind of mutagen to use depends on the kind of mutation you want, and how long you want to spend looking for it. Chemical mutagens are most suitable for obtaining point mutations (or small, intragenic deletions) at a reasonable rate. Thus, they are best for obtaining an allelic series or conditional (e.g., temperature-sensitive) mutations, and for screens aimed at obtaining predefined phenotypes (e.g., learning mutants). Radiation is most suitable for producing rearrangements, i.e., translocations, duplications, deletions, and inversions. Insertional mutagenesis gives the best leverage for rapid molecular cloning of the mutated gene. Its derivative, enhancer trapping, allows the identification of genes on the basis of enhancer-driven expression patterns.

A detailed account of various mutagens, their properties, and uses can be found in the Ashburner (1989) commentaries. The following account is abbreviated.

## Ethylmethane Sulfonate (EMS)

EMS is the most commonly used chemical mutagen. It is an alkylating agent that produces a high proportion of point mutations, although it also produces small deletions and, occasionally, other rearrangements as well. The dose required depends on the kind of screen, such that a lower dose is required when searching for a new mutation, and higher doses can be used for isolating new alleles of existing mutations. This is because the chromosome is to be made homozygous in the former case, whereas it will be tested in trans with another chromosome in the latter. The rationale is that when making treated chromosomes homozygous to look for a particular phenotype, you do not want to complicate the situation by having more than one homozygous mutation present—especially a recessive lethal mutation.

For a low dose, males are fed a solution of 2.5 mM EMS in 1% sucrose overnight (see Ashburner 1989). This results in an average of one lethal hit per chromosome arm, or a rate of 1 hit per 1000 chromosome arms per locus. (That is, if you test progeny from a mutagenized male, you will find an average of one new lethal mutation on each individual's $X$. If you are screening for mutations at a particular locus, you will find it in approximately 1 out of 1000 chromosomes screened. This corresponds to the fact that there are roughly 1000 lethally mutable genes on each of the major chromosome arms [$X$, $2L$, $2R$, $3L$, $3R$].) A twofold higher dose may be used for screens in which treated chromosomes are scored when heterozygous (as in a screen for new mutations uncovered by a deletion).

The treated flies are mated to females for 4–5 days, after which time the males are removed. This is done to maximize the proportion of uniquely mutant chromosomes, since the mutagen can affect gonial stem cells as well as mature sperm. When gonial cells are affected, multiple sperm with the same mutation are produced. Since the stem cells are less sensitive, the overall frequency of individual hits will be lower. To avoid this, the treated males are discarded before stem cell daughters have had time to become mature sperm, thus ensuring that mutations will be independently induced. The virtue of having independently induced mutations is that you don't waste time analyzing the same allele more than once. Additionally, when attempting saturation mutagenesis, the only way to estimate when saturation has been attained is by the frequency of repeated, independent mutations of the same locus.

As an alkylating agent, EMS acts on one strand of the double helix. This means that F1 progeny will be mosaic, at least to some extent, for the new mutation. In practice, this only matters when trying to score a mutant phenotype in the F1, since then the new mutation must be present in the germ cells as well as in the somatic tissues you have scored, and a somatic phenotype can be detected even when all cells might not be mutant.

It is best to treat males that are 3–5 days old, when they will mate most readily. But watch out: Many will not survive the overnight exposure to mutagen, not all will be fertile after the treatment, and many of the F1 progeny males will be sterile. It is thus a good rule of thumb to mutagenize a large number of males—equal to half the number of F1 individuals you plan to test cross (see below). Equally wise is to run a pilot first to assess the mutagen-sensitivity of the flies you are actually planning to use. Another virtue of a pilot run is that it tells whether your crosses will produce the classes of progeny you expect. Many ideas look great on paper but fail utterly when it comes to real flies.

### Ethylnitrosourea (ENU)

We assume, for operational purposes, that chemical mutagens like EMS are completely random in their site of action. This is not true, in fact, and nowhere has it been revealed more clearly than in the different spectrum of mutations obtained with another alkylating agent, ENU. With ENU, the mutability of genes is different and the kinds of mutations obtained are different, although the overall frequency is comparable. The frequency of rearrangements also appears to be reduced, as does the frequency of mosaicism in the F1 progeny. In all other respects, the same principles and practices apply as with EMS. A feeding dose of 7.5 mM produces lethals (standard jargon for "lethal mutations") on approximately 40% of the treated chromosome arms.

ENU is even more hazardous for us mammals than EMS: It causes an extraordinarily high frequency of brain tumors in mice. Many fly people do not consider its benefits worth the added risk and the extreme precautions it requires.

### Radiation

Radiation in the form of X-rays was the first mutagen ever to be used, and it remains an essential tool for geneticists. The most conveniently available sources of radiation are X-ray machines and cobalt or cesium sources (for gamma rays). All are capable of inducing chromosome breaks which are then sometimes repaired so as to produce translocations, deletions, transpositions, and inversions. The breakpoints that comprise these rearrangements also cause mutant phenotypes if they fall within a gene or if, by juxtaposing certain chromosome regions, they produce a phenomenon known as "position effect" (see Ashburner 1989). Radiation also causes point mutations some of the time.

Mature sperm are the most susceptible target for irradiation. The possible range of rearrangements produced by irradiation of mature sperm is limited by the fact that each sperm has only a haploid set of chromosomes. Thus, events involving pairs of homologs (including the $X$ and $Y$) cannot occur.

The frequency of these events is considerably lower than for chemical mutagenesis. A dose of 4000r to males yields a frequency of roughly 5% lethal hits (i.e., lethal mutations) per chromosome arm as opposed to 60% with the standard dose of EMS. This dose is calibrated as the highest dose that does not cause excessive sterility. Since the breakage event is double-stranded, there are no problems with mosaicism in the progeny. Otherwise, the flies are handled similarly as with chemical mutagens.

## Insertional Mutagenesis

Disruption of genes by the insertion of transposable elements is not the easiest form of mutagenesis, but the advantages conferred by having an insertion to "tag" a gene or an enhancer trap to reveal an expression pattern often outweigh the inconveniences. The principle is that of mobilizing a mobile element to transpose and reintegrate at a new site in the genome; this is also known as hybrid dysgenesis. P-elements have been the most commonly used transposons, with Hobo a recent addition. (The abovementioned "inconveniences" may wither away as the Fly Genome Project proceeds and facilitates the detailed mapping and identification of any and all molecular lesions.)

P-element mutagenesis may be carried out either with intact transposons, starting with strains carrying many such elements in their genome, or with various kinds of inactive elements capable of being transposed, but lacking the activity itself. Inactive elements must be activated by the addition of the transposase activity separately, usually in the form of a chromosome carrying a stably integrated transposase gene.

The advantage of the inactive elements is that the induction of jumps can be controlled by simply adding and removing the transposase activity through appropriate crosses (see below). The equivalent of a mutagenized male in this technique is the progeny from a cross that brings together the transposable element and the transposase activity in the same fly. Each sperm in these males is treated as if unique, just as if the fly had been fed a mutagen. In subsequent generations, there is no mosaicism to be resolved, just the separation of transposase activity from transposable elements to prevent further jumps.

The frequency of jumps is a combination of (1) the frequency of excisions, which seems to depend in a somewhat unpredictable way on the size and sequences present in the transposon as well as the site of insertion, and (2) the frequency of insertions, which depends in a totally unpredictable way on the sequences present at a given locus. Some loci are hot spots for insertions, such as the singed (*sn*) locus where insertions occur at a rate of roughly 1/100. Other loci seem to be completely refractory to insertions, such as alcohol dehydrogenase (*Adh*). The overall average is roughly 1/2000. Part of the rationale for developing an alternative to P-elements, the Hobo system, was to exploit a different set of insertion biases (Smith et al. 1993).

## GENETIC SCHEMES FOR DETECTING MUTANTS

Tests for new mutations vary with the situation but usually fall into two categories: those that are concerned with a particular locus or chromosome region and those that are focused on a particular phenotype irrespective of where the genes map. The first kind involves testing the treated chromosome in heterozygous condition—usually in *trans* with a known mutation or deletion-bearing chromosome. The second kind requires that the treated chromosomes be made homozygous.

### New Alleles at an Autosomal Locus

A frequent source of insight into a gene's action comes from the analysis of an allelic series. The more complex the process in which a gene is involved, the more important such analyses become. The basic strategy is the classic complementation test, in which the newly mutagenized chromosome is made heterozygous with a known allele of the locus in question. Crucial to this strategy is the ability to distinguish the chromosome bearing the new allele from the old. A simple scheme for isolating new alleles of a recessive lethal, third-chromosome mutation (naked cuticle, *nkd*) is shown:

Mutagenize wild-type males, mass mate to virgins carrying a balancer *TM6* marked with the dominant mutation *Ubx*, heterozygous with a different dominant marker *Sb*. Actually, one rarely uses wild-type males, instead using males homozygous for some gratuitous marker such as the cuticle color mutation ebony *(e)*.

♂♂ $\dfrac{e}{e}$ × $\dfrac{TM6,\ Ubx}{Sb}$ balancer ♀♀
dominant

↓

Produces

$\dfrac{e}{TM6,\ Ubx}$ and $\dfrac{e}{Sb}$ F1 progeny, both ♂♂ and ♀♀

Of the two types of F1 progeny produced, one is *Ubx*, but not *Sb* (i.e., it is *Sb⁺*) and the other is *Sb* but not *Ubx* (i.e., it is *Ubx⁺*). Select the males that are *Sb*, *Ubx⁺* and mate them individually to virgins carrying *nkd* balanced by *TM3, Ser*.

♂ $\dfrac{e^*}{Sb}$ × $\dfrac{nkd}{TM3,\ Ser}$ ♀♀

↓

F2 progeny will be one of these four genotypes (both ♂♂ and ♀♀):

| $\dfrac{e^*}{nkd}$ | $\dfrac{e^*}{TM3,\ Ser}$ | $\dfrac{Sb}{nkd}$ | $\dfrac{Sb}{TM3,\ Ser}$ |
|---|---|---|---|
| **Progeny class:**   1 | 2 | 3 | 4 |
| neither Ser nor Sb (*Ser⁺ Sb⁺*) | *Ser* but not *Sb* (*Ser Sb⁺*) | *Sb* but not *Ser* (*Sb Ser⁺*) | both *Sb* and *Ser* (*Sb Ser*) |

As always, the shorthand shows the genotypes of the relevant pairs of homologs, but the genotypes of all classes of progeny are uncharacteristically drawn out. This scheme illustrates the principle of "cloning" of mutagenized chromosomes (symbolized by an asterisk*). The first mating is done en masse, since every sperm from a mutagenized male is genetically

unique. Each of their F1 progeny now carries a single set of mutagenized chromosomes and so can be tested for the presence of the desired mutation by mating males singly to several virgin females. (The number of males to mutagenize at the outset should be based on the number of these individual F1 males you plan to test-cross. That is, you should mutagenize twice as many males at the beginning as you plan to test-cross at this stage. The decision on how many to test-cross at this stage will depend on how much of your time you want to spend on this mutagenesis.) The "wild-type" males carry a gratuitous marker mutation (*e*, in this case) to aid in identifying the mutagenized chromosome in subsequent tests of homozygous survival or just to guard against the introduction of spurious chromosomes from stray flies that might contaminate a stock.

This scheme also illustrates the principle of making each genotype unambiguously identifiable. Each class of progeny can be easily recognized by the presence or absence of the dominant markers Stubble (*Sb*) and Serrate (*Ser*). (F1 males carrying *Ubx* instead of *Sb* could also be used.) Class 1 has none of the dominant markers. *If no class 1 progeny are found, you have induced a new mutation that fails to complement the lethality of nkd.* These will be rare, and so the majority of the vial crosses will have class 1 as 25% of the progeny, with no abnormalities. This class is also where new, viable alleles of *nkd* will be seen, if they are recognizable; that is, they may or may not differ phenotypically from the original *nkd* allele.

If one or more of the vials indicate the presence of a new mutation, the scheme also provides a convenient way of recovering that chromosome without having to worry whether the original male is still alive. (In fact, he is almost certainly no longer alive, since you undoubtedly dumped him and his harem into your morgue prior to the emergence of the F2 generation.) The flies carrying the new mutation are recognizable as class 2 progeny, those who inherited the dominant marker *Ser* (but not *Sb*) carried by their mothers on the balancer chromosome *TM3*.

The key feature shown here is the use of two different dominants in the second cross, such that they "trade" markers. That is, in the F1 generation, *Sb* marks the progeny carrying the mutagenized chromosome (*e**). Similarly, the females that the F1 males mate with are carrying the test mutation (*nkd*) heterozygous with a different dominant (*Ser*). Since these dominant markers will segregate from their respective homologs carrying these mutations in the next generation, you can be assured that F2 progeny carrying *Ser* (but not *Sb*) will also carry *e**, whereas those carrying *Sb* (but not *Ser*) will also carry the original *nkd*. Thus, they have "traded" markers. This is one of the most useful techniques for identifying genotypes, especially since most of the mutations you will work with are recessive and thus invisible in heterozygous condition. As described previously, its success depends on the absence of recombination in males and the suppression of recombination by balancer chromosomes in females.

A final point about this scheme is that it allows you to set up a true-breeding stock of heterozygotes for the new lethal mutation. By collecting males and virgin females of class 2 (*TM3, Ser/e*+), a "balanced" stock can be started in which the only viable progeny will have the same genotype as their parents; homozygotes for either chromosome are nonviable.

### New Alleles on the *X*

Picking up new alleles of a locus is straightforward on the autosomes but can be difficult on the *X* if the new alleles are lethal in males. This derives from the unavoidable fact that males have only one *X*, which exposes any recessive mutations to full expression. A male carrying a lethal on its *X* is in big trouble when it comes to propagating.

The test of a newly induced mutation for allelism must involve complementation. To introduce the mutant allele from both parents, a way must be found to allow the survival of males carrying it. The easiest solution is to use a duplication of the normal chromosomal region containing the locus. This can be an insertion of the region into either the *Y* chromosome or an autosome, and such duplications do exist for many parts of the *X*. (They can also be made for unrepresented parts; see Chapter 4.) A representative scheme for isolating new alleles of the *X*-linked lethal armadillo (*arm*) is shown below. The "wild-type" males to be mutagenized start out with the gratuitous *X*-chromosome marker yellow (*y*):

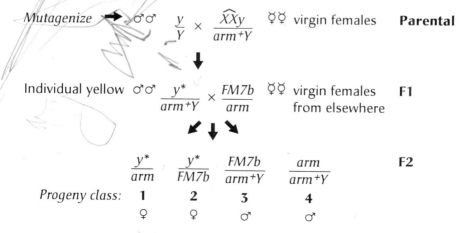

This scheme illustrates several features that are peculiar to the $X$. Focusing on the parental (**P**) cross that produces the **F1** generation, the $\widehat{XX}/arm^+Y$ females in the first cross carry an attached-$X$ marked with yellow ($y$) and also a $Y$ chromosome, one that has a duplication of the wild-type armadillo locus on it. (Recall that the presence of a $Y$ chromosome in females affects neither their femaleness nor their fertility.) In this situation, the $Y$ chromosome will segregate from the attached-$X$ at meiosis so that progeny from the cross will inherit either the attached-$X$ or the $arm^+Y$ from their mother. When fertilized by sperm carrying either of the father's sex chromosomes, the resulting progeny of the first cross above are these:

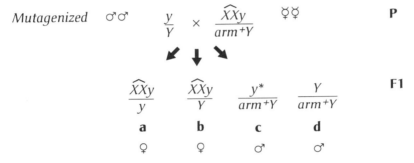

Only two of these genotypes, **b** and **c**, are potentially viable. **a** with three $X$s and **d** with no $X$ are lethal. **b** is female, having inherited the mother's attached-$X$ and the father's $Y$, whereas **c** has the normal chromosome constitution of a male.

> **PROBLEM 1**   Show how this represents a reversal of the normal transmission of $X$ and $Y$ from parents to offspring by predicting the genotypes from a cross of a wild-type male with a female of the genotype $w/FM7b$.

For the purposes of our mutagenesis, class **c** in the F1 generation contains males with a mutagenized $X$ chromosome and a $Y$ duplication that "covers" armadillo (i.e., it contains a wild-type copy of it that rescues the mutant phenotype). This means that if the $X$ carries a newly induced mutation of $arm$, the male will be rescued by the $arm^+Y$. (If it carries a new lethal mutation outside of the region covered by the duplication, it will not survive, but then you wouldn't want it anyway.)

In the F2 generation, the class 1 progeny will constitute the complementation test for a new allele of armadillo: $y^*/arm$. By the same token, this new chromosome is recoverable in the sibling females of class 2, balanced by the *FM7b* chromosome. A stock that is effectively true-breeding can then be set up by simply mating the females of class 2 (as virgins) to *FM7b/Y* males. (The balancer *FM7b* carries the *lz$^{sp}$* allele of lozenge, which confers female sterility when homozygous, so that homozygous *FM7b* females produce no progeny. Thus, the only productive matings will be between *FM7b/Y* males and *y\*/FM7b* females.

> **PROBLEM 2** How could you carry out a similar screen without resorting to an attached-*X*? Also, how could you do it using an insertion of *arm$^+$* into an autosome (*Dp(1;2) arm$^+$*) instead of an *arm$^+$Y*?

## Identifying New Genes by Mutagenesis

Much of our contemporary picture of the genetic control of pattern formation in the fly embryo is derived from the panel of mutants isolated by Wieschaus and Nüsslein-Volhard in the late 1970s. Their strategy is a classic illustration of using a mutant screen to identify new genes based on phenotype. The only assumption made was that there are mutable genes which will alter the cuticle pattern of mature embryos. One of the principal strengths of the approach is its lack of bias—any molecular component that contributes to this process is fair game—and this has been borne out by the identification of genes as diverse as transcription factors, receptor tyrosine kinases, and tight junction molecules.

The screens were designed to reveal loci anywhere on each chromosome affecting cuticular phenotype. In order to do this, they needed to generate many lines containing homozygous, mutagenized chromosomes and then have a simple and rapid method of screening for pattern alterations in them. The basic strategy behind these screens, widely applicable to many situations, is outlined below.

### Isogenize the Starter Stock

Since the scheme relies on screening for lethal mutations in homozygous lines, it is very important that the strain to be mutagenized does not start out with lethal mutations in it. This may seem a trivial concern at first glance, since obviously if you start with live flies from a homozygous stock, there must not be any lethals present. But the genetics gods are not so kind, and although the spontaneous mutation rate is low enough to be ignored most of the time, it is not zero. Spontaneous mutations will occur in any culture. They can become predominant as a result of genetic drift in small culture populations, such as those in a vial. Some of these will be recessive lethals, and some of the live flies will carry them in heterozygous condition. If as few as 1% of the flies carry these, when this stock is used as the source of "wild-type" chromosomes for the mutagenesis, the vast majority of supposedly new mutations isolated will be the ones preexisting in the stock. Although this may be a fine project for a recalcitrant undergraduate or for the son of the Dean whom you "volunteered" to take into the lab for the summer, it is really not a worthwhile way to spend time.

The preventive steps are easy: Isogenize the starter stock. That is, start a new stock from a single chromosome, then use it promptly before the genetics gods can do their mischief (i.e., within a month or so). A simple scheme for isogenizing a second chromosome is shown below. (The chromosome carries eye-color markers cinnabar [*cn*] and brown [*bw*], which together produce a white-eyed fly. This facilitates the scoring of lethals later in the mutagenesis screen for chromosome 2.) For isogenization of the second chromosome:

$$\sigma\sigma \quad \frac{cn\ bw}{cn\ bw} \quad \times \quad \frac{In(2LR)O,Cy}{Sco} \quad \text{♀♀}$$

| | | |
|---|---|---|
| Select *Cy*, not *Sco*, males (use one per vial) | $\sigma \quad \dfrac{In(2LR)O,Cy}{cn\ bw} \quad \times \quad \dfrac{In(2LR)O,Cy}{Sco} \quad$ ♀♀ | **F1** |
| From within the same vial | $\sigma\sigma \quad \dfrac{In(2LR)O,Cy}{cn\ bw} \quad \times \quad \dfrac{In(2LR)O,Cy}{cn\ bw} \quad$ ♀♀ | **F2** |
| Select *cn bw* homozygotes ♂♂ and ♀♀ | $\dfrac{cn\ bw}{cn\ bw}$ | **F3** |

In the F1 stage of the scheme, a single *cn bw* chromosome is being propagated. All the progeny in the F2 generation carry the same *cn bw* chromosome, which cannot recombine with its homolog, the balancer *In(2LR)O,Cy*. By the F3 generation, the stock is isogenic. It is wise to set up more than one vial at the F1 stage, since all your work will be for naught if there is a lethal lurking on the one *cn bw* chromosome you choose—and you can rest assured that if you only set up one male, **he** will be carrying a lethal. In addition to ensuring that the *cn bw* chromosome is viable, you should also monitor how healthy it is by counting the proportion of *cn bw* progeny in each vial you set up as compared to the *In(2LR)O,Cy* progeny. If healthy, the ratio of *cn bw:In(2LR)O,Cy* should be 1:2.

**PROBLEM 3** Why is it unnecessary to carry out these steps before an *X*-chromosome screen?

*The Mutagenesis Screen*

Now back to the mutagenesis; this little detour has only set you back by 8 weeks, which gave you enough time to expand the other stocks to the level needed for a large-scale screen. It will have also given you time to test all other stocks you are going to use to make sure they have the right chromosomes and behave properly (more later). The scheme is illustrated below:

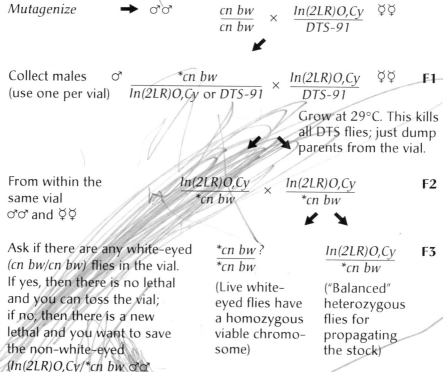

*Mutagenize* ➡ ♂♂ $\dfrac{cn\ bw}{cn\ bw}$ × $\dfrac{In(2LR)O,Cy}{DTS\text{-}91}$ ♀♀

Collect males ♂ $\dfrac{*cn\ bw}{In(2LR)O,Cy\ or\ DTS\text{-}91}$ × $\dfrac{In(2LR)O,Cy}{DTS\text{-}91}$ ♀♀ **F1**

(use one per vial)

Grow at 29°C. This kills all DTS flies; just dump parents from the vial.

From within the same vial ♂♂ and ♀♀ $\dfrac{In(2LR)O,Cy}{*cn\ bw}$ × $\dfrac{In(2LR)O,Cy}{*cn\ bw}$ **F2**

Ask if there are any white-eyed (*cn bw/cn bw*) flies in the vial. If yes, then there is no lethal and you can toss the vial; if no, then there is a new lethal and you want to save the non-white-eyed (*In(2LR)O,Cy/*cn bw* ♂♂ and ♀♀) flies to start a balanced lethal stock.

$\dfrac{*cn\ bw\ ?}{*cn\ bw}$

(Live white-eyed flies have a homozygous viable chromosome)

$\dfrac{In(2LR)O,Cy}{*cn\ bw}$ **F3**

("Balanced" heterozygous flies for propagating the stock)

In principle, this scheme is very similar to the one just used to isogenize the *cn bw* chromosome. Mutagenize males that carry marked chromosomes (*cn bw*), cross them to females with a balancer chromosome and another dominantly marked chromosome, derive unique mutagenized chromosomes in the F1 males that are heterozygous with either the balancer (*In(2LR)O,Cy*) or the dominant-bearing chromosome (*DTS-91*), cross these F1 males to females from the same balancer/dominant stock, and then make the mutagenized chromosomes homozygous.

What distinguishes this scheme from the one described earlier is the use of a dominant temperature-sensitive (DTS) lethal. As the name implies, this chromosome carries a mutation that kills all progeny that carry it at the nonpermissive temperature of 29°C. It acts during development, so the bottles must be shifted to the high temperature after eggs are laid to be effective. The value of a DTS in this scheme is that it obviates the need to collect virgins at the F2 generation—which would be brutal to do for 1,000 vials, let alone 10,000. Instead, the DTS kills all but the *\*cn bw/In(2LR)O,Cy* progeny. Just by dumping parents from the vial, those progeny will constitute the crucial cross in which the *\*cn bw* chromosomes become homozygous. This leaves the F1 cross as the only stage requiring a large amount of effort at virgin collecting. (Balancer chromosomes with DTS on them have also been made. They are particularly useful for generating homozygotes automatically, as in screens for maternal effect mutations in which homozygous mutant females must be generated to be tested.) DTS techniques will interfere with efforts to find temperature-sensitive mutations.

When the F3 progeny appear, you merely have to look at the vial to see if there are any white-eyed progeny. If there are, the *\*cn bw* chromosome does not carry a new lethal, and the vial can be thrown out. If there are none, you may have a new lethal, already balanced. On the other hand, if you are looking for viable mutations, this tells you to save the vial.

There are some pitfalls in this scheme, but a little caution will keep you from falling in. First, the reason for saying only that you "may" have a new lethal is that there may not have been enough progeny in the vial to be certain that there were no *\*cn bw/\*cn bw* progeny. Expanding the stock in the next generation will resolve the issue. Second, it is crucial to dump parents before the emergence of progeny at each generation, so that you are only performing the crosses you intended. Finally, DTS stocks must be tested before you start the scheme, to ensure that they work and that they are not leaky. (This principle actually applies to all stocks used in any fly mutagenesis. A little paranoia never hurt.)

The virtues of mutagenizing a marked chromosome like *cn bw* are several. The ease of lethal detection has already been mentioned. The two markers also make it easy to carry out a preliminary mapping of the new mutation (see Chapter 3). Finally, they help guard against your "re-isolating" a mutation that someone else is working with in the lab. Flies do escape and contaminate other crosses occasionally. If your mutagenized chromosomes are distinctly marked, you won't accidentally pick up your benchmate's mutant line by cross-contamination (unless that stock has the same markers, or unless this is the only way you can get your benchmate to give you his mutant line). Although this may sound unlikely, it has actually occurred enough times to be taken seriously. Sometimes, the error was not discovered until the "new alleles" were sequenced and found to be identical to the original.

Lethals are not the only possible products of such a screen. The homozygous *\*cn bw/\*cn bw* progeny of the F3 may carry all sorts of viable but nonetheless interesting mutations—death is not the only interesting phenotype to study in flies.

*Screening the X for New Genes*

Given the special problems of handling lethals on the *X*, it should come as no surprise that Wieschaus and Nüsslein-Volhard had to devise an efficient scheme for screening the *X*:

Mutagenized $\quad\quad$ ♂♂ $\quad \dfrac{y}{Y} \quad \times \quad \dfrac{FM7\text{-}TW9}{\text{"any lethal"}}$ ♀♀

Take individual $\quad$ ♀ $\quad \dfrac{y^*}{FM7\text{-}TW9} \quad \times \quad \dfrac{FM7}{Y}$ ♂♂ $\quad$ Brought in
females (one per vial) $\qquad\qquad\qquad\qquad\qquad\qquad\qquad\qquad$ from outside

Check vials for presence of
$y^*$ males. If yes, toss vial;
if no, you've got a new lethal,
balanced with *FM7-TW9*.

This is simple, but eloquent. The genotype of virgins in the first cross, *FM7-TW9/"any lethal"*, is the key to this scheme. *FM7-TW9* is a variant of the *X*-chromosome balancer *FM7* which has had a recessive lethal induced on it by Ted Wright (hence the "TW"). The other chromosome can carry any other lethal, so that these females are alive but will produce no viable male progeny. This has therefore become a "virginizing" cross because the only viable progeny will be females, and therefore virgins. This means that you can collect *y/FM7-TW9 virgins from these vials at your leisure and mate them individually to FM7 males. If a new lethal has been induced on the *y chromosome, this cross will produce no viable y males, and it will be balanced.

This scheme carries with it the usual caveat that you must get enough progeny ($\geq$ 25 for a first pass, then re-test with more the next generation) to believe that there are no yellow males. Since the cross is being started with only one female, this confirmation in the next generation becomes all the more important. Similarly, not as many of the vial crosses will go with only one female starting them. This is not fatal to the scheme, only to the particular flies, and can be anticipated by starting more vials than is usual.

## Insertional Mutagenesis and Enhancer Trapping

Not long after the inception of P-element transformation in *Drosophila*, the potential use of transposable elements for insertional or "tagged" mutagenesis became apparent to many in the fly world. It started out as a cottage industry, using simple transformation vectors carrying either the wild-type allele of the eye-color gene rosy ($ry^+$) or the bacterial neomycin gene for resistance to the drug G418 ($neo^+$) (Cooley et al. 1988). With the development of "enhancer-trap" P-elements (O'Kane and Gehring 1987; Bellen et al. 1989; Bier et al. 1989) expressing $\beta$-galactosidase (*lacZ*) in a tissue-specific manner depending on the site of insertion, the cottage industry grew into a multinational conglomerate. Now there is hardly a fly lab that has not generated at least one enhancer-trap line of its own.

The initial appeal of insertional mutants was the ease of cloning the disrupted gene, a process made even easier by the inclusion of plasmid rescue sequences inside the incorporated vector (Bier et al. 1989; Wilson et al. 1989). This advantage compensated for the considerably lower frequency of mutagenesis (see earlier in chapter). In other words, the technique was simply another way of mutagenizing. With the advent of enhancer trapping, an altogether new strategy for identifying genes has emerged, based on pattern of expression rather than on mutant phenotype. New insertion lines can be generated in large numbers and screened very easily, since the position-dependent expression of *lacZ* does not require homozygosity of the insert. Lines that show "interesting" patterns of expression can then be saved and made homozygous to see if the insertion has disrupted a gene capable of producing an obvious phenotype.

Schemes for mobilizing P-elements and recovering new insertion lines resemble the standard mutagenesis schemes in many respects, with the new wrinkle of genetically introducing the elements that do the mobilizing and that are mobilized, instead of administering a physical or chemical mutagen. There are two separate genetic elements that are used: a transposable element and a "transposase" activity to catalyze the excision and insertion events. (Both of these elements were originally part of the same primordial P-element, which catalyzed its own movements. For convenience they have been separated.)

## Enhancer-trap Screens

The transposable elements used in enhancer trapping consist of P-element flanking sequences, capable of being acted on by the transposase, within which are included *lacZ*, a wild-type eye-color gene for detecting the element (either *rosy*, $ry^+$, or *white*, $w^+$) and plasmid rescue sequences (usually ampicillin resistance and an *E. coli* origin of replication). The $w^+$ used in these vectors is a "mini-gene," whose expression and subsequent eye color are also affected by the site of insertion so that it is often possible to distinguish homozygotes from heterozygotes, as well as to differentiate between various lines by eye color. To make life even easier, the transposable element can be excised from a balancer chromosome, such as *In(2LR)O,Cy, P[ArB]A4.1M2*, a variant of *In(2LR)O,Cy* containing a *lacZ*, $ry^+$ enhancer-trap vector (also written as *P[lacZ, $ry^+$]*). In this way, all of the chromosomes that contain the original, unmobilized element can be effectively screened out in the next generation by selecting $Cy^+$ progeny. The source of transposase is a defective P-element that is stably integrated into the third chromosome near the right tip, *P[$ry^+$Δ2-3]* (known less formally as Δ2-3) because of its deletion of the intron between ORF2 and ORF3 (Robertson et al. 1988). Usually, this is introduced on a chromosome also carrying the dominant bristle mutation Stubble (*Sb*) for easy detection of its presence.

The approach relies on the ability of the *P[$ry^+$Δ2-3]* element to mobilize the transposable element when they are present together in the male or female germ cells. A "mutagenic" male is produced by crossing flies carrying each element separately. By introducing them on different chromosomes, it is possible to limit the conjunction of the transposase and the transposable element to a single generation, so that one does not confound the isolation of single new insertions by the continual generation of a heterogeneous population of new transpositions within each line. Absence of the transposase is monitored by scoring for $Sb^+$; this only works if the chromosome carrying $P[ry^+\Delta 2\text{-}3]$ and $Sb$ is not permitted to recombine with its homolog, an event that might separate the marker $Sb$ from the transposase. It is accomplished by making sure that it is balanced when in a female (i.e., heterozygous with a balancer chromosome like $TM6$, $Ubx$) or else kept in a male in which recombination does not occur.

Presence of the transposable element is monitored by scoring for the wild-type eye-color marker contained in the element (either $ry^+$ or $w^+$). When this element has been jumped out of a balancer like $In(2LR)O,Cy$, it becomes possible to select only those progeny containing a new insertion site simply by picking flies carrying the wild-type eye-color marker and lacking $Cy$. This necessitates, of course, that the normal loci for $ry$ or $w$ are mutant. A representative "jump-starter" scheme is shown below:

$$\male\male \quad \frac{In(2LR)O,Cy, P[lacZ, ry^+]}{+} ; \frac{ry^{506}}{ry^{506}} \quad \times \quad \frac{Sb\ P[ry^+\Delta\ 2\text{-}3]}{TM6,\ Ubx} \qquad \female\female \quad P$$

These males are $Cy$.                    These virgins are $Sb$ and $Ubx$.

Select  $\male\male$  $\dfrac{In(2LR)O,Cy, P[lacZ, ry^+]}{+}$ ; $\dfrac{Sb\ P[ry^+\Delta\ 2\text{-}3]}{ry^{506}}$ $\times$ $\dfrac{ry^{506}}{ry^{506}}$ $\female\female$ **F1**

$Cy\ Sb\ Ubx^+$
males, which
are dysgenic,
and mate to
$ry$ virgins.

Select single $ry^+\ Cy^+\ Sb^+$       $\dfrac{+^*}{Y} ; \dfrac{+^*}{+} ; \dfrac{ry^{506*}}{ry^{506}}$  or  $\dfrac{+^*}{+} ; \dfrac{+^*}{+} ; \dfrac{ry^{506*}}{ry^{506}}$     **F2**
males or females; they will
have possible insertions (*).
$\qquad\qquad\qquad\qquad\qquad \male \qquad\qquad\qquad\qquad \female$

This scheme starts with males heterozygous for a second chromosome $In(2LR)O,Cy$ balancer containing the P-element with $lacZ$ and the wild-type allele of rosy $(ry^+)$ in it, and homozygous on the third chromosome for the rosy allele $ry^{506}$. These are mated to virgins heterozygous on the third chromosome for $Sb\ P[ry^+\Delta 2\text{-}3]$, the source of transposase activity, and the balancer $TM6$. The purpose of this cross is to obtain F1 males carrying the $In(2LR)O,Cy, P[lacZ, ry^+]$ chromosome and the $Sb\ P[ry^+\Delta 2\text{-}3]$ chromosome because it is in these males that hybrid dysgenesis will occur, resulting in the transposition of the P-element to new sites on any chromosome. To detect and recover these transposition events, these F1 males are mated to homozygous $ry^{506}$ virgins. It is essential to maintain homozygosity for $ry^{506}$ on the third chromosome so that the $ry^+$ P-element will be detectable on the basis of its ability to provide $ry^+$ activity.

In the F2 generation, one selects for flies that have a new insertion of the P-element and that no longer have the transposase activity that could otherwise continue to destabilize the P-elements. These are recognizable as those flies that do not have $Sb$ (and consequently do not have $P[ry^+\Delta2\text{-}3]$) and those that do not have $Cy$ in order to get rid of the original sources of the $ry^+$ P-element, the $In(2LR)O,Cy$, $P[lacZ, ry^+]$ chromosome. The absence of the original $In(2LR)O,Cy$, $P[lacZ, ry^+]$ chromosome permits the detection of the presence of the P-element on a new chromosome because the new insert will be the only source of $ry^+$ activity. This is why it is essential to maintain homozygosity for $ry^{506}$ at the third chromosome $ry$ locus. The $+^*$ symbols represent the $X$ and second chromosomes, and $ry^{506*}$ represents the third chromosome derived from the F1 dysgenic males. These are the chromosomes that could contain new insertions of $P[lacZ, ry^+]$.

Any new insertion can be propagated simply by continuing to select $ry^+$ progeny and mating them to $ry^{506}$ homozygotes. For lines that you want to keep, or to test for viability by making homozygous, it is essential to determine the chromosomal linkage of the insert and to balance it. For this purpose, it is useful to construct homozygous $ry^{506}$ stocks that carry $FM7$ or $In(2LR)O,Cy$, and for the third chromosome there are balancers, $TM3$, $ry^{RK}$ $Sb$ $e$ and $TM2$, $ry$ $Ubx$, that contain a rosy mutation. One then simply does a linkage test (see Chapter 3) by mating the insert-bearing flies to one of the balancer stocks, picking up progeny carrying both the insert and the balancer, then seeing if they always segregate from each other in the next generation. If so, the insert is linked to the homolog of the balancer. ($ry^{506}$ is the allele most traditionally used in P-element schemes because it is healthy and not spontaneously revertible, due to a small internal deletion of the rosy gene.)

> **PROBLEM 4** Design the crosses for determining linkage and testing homozygous viability of a newly mobilized $w^+$ insert. Figure out what stocks you will need for the tests and work out the expected results for inserts on each of the four chromosomes.

## New Insertional Alleles of Known Loci

If the goal is to produce a new insertional allele of an existing mutation, the scheme needs to be modified in order to maximize the number of jumps in each germ cell and to set up a complementation test for putative new insertions at the locus. Given the low frequency of inserts at most loci, this means that it is important to start out with as many transposable elements as possible to optimize the chances of getting a hit in the desired gene. For this purpose, a chromosome exists known as Birmingham-2 (*Birm2*), a second chromosome containing 17 P-elements that are capable of being transposed, but lacking in wild-type transposase activity themselves (Bingham et al. 1982). There is a trade-off, however, in the extra amount of work required later on to track and identify the right P-element insertion when it is unmarked. An alternative chromosome, available from the Bloomington Stock Center, has been constructed to mitigate this problem: an attached-*X* with eight *P[w⁺]* inserts (D. Lindsley, pers. comm.; Bloomington Stock #3697 and #16). These P-elements have plasmid rescue sequences as well as the *w⁺* marker to be even more labor-saving. The disadvantage, if any, is that there are fewer elements to jump and they don't jump with as high a frequency as those in *Birm2*. C'est la vie.

The first cross is the same as in enhancer trapping, designed to put the *Birm2* chromosome together with the *Sb P[ry⁺Δ2-3]* chromosome in the F1 males' germ cells. From this point on, it is just like the mutagenesis schemes described previously for use with chemical mutagens: cloning and complementation testing of the relevant chromosomes from the mutagenic male. The only variation is that one must select against the *Sb P[ry⁺Δ2-3]* chromosome in the next generation to guard against ongoing element mobilization (as discussed above). Since one is concentrating on a single locus and since these elements do not carry a wild-type eye-color marker, there is no need to worry about tracking them genetically.

**PROBLEM 5** Design a scheme to isolate an insertional allele of the third chromosome recessive lethal mutation canoe (*cno*). Use the *Birm2* chromosome, which can be kept homozygous, and any other chromosome described thus far.

At the end of one of these schemes, it is essential to "clean up" the chromosome containing the new mutation, since it will almost certainly contain more than just one insertion. By doing this, you also dilute out other P-elements on other chromosomes. Since the whole purpose of using insertions is to clone the locus, multiple insertions will confound the cloning. The cleanup is best done by subjecting the chromosome to free recombination to allow the undesired inserts to recombine away, followed by re-isolation of the mutation-bearing chromosome.

$$\male\male \quad \frac{[P][P][P][{}^*P][P][P]}{TM3} \quad \times \quad \frac{+}{+} \quad \female\female$$

$$\downarrow$$

Unbalanced, $\quad \female\female \quad \dfrac{[P][P][P][{}^*P][P][P]}{+} \quad \times \quad \dfrac{TM6,Ubx}{Sb} \quad \male\male$
heterozygous F1
females subject
to free recombination

Select individual $\quad \male \quad \dfrac{[{}^*P]}{TM6,\ Ubx\ or\ Sb} \quad \times \quad \dfrac{TM3,\ Ser}{lethal} \quad \female\female$
males, *Ubx* or *Sb*

The principle here is to generate females heterozygous for the P-element-bearing chromosome and a normal chromosome. These will be subject to free recombination and will produce unique recombinant chromosomes (since each meiosis is different) that can be recovered in individual F1 males balanced with *TM6* or heterozygous with *Sb*. These F1 males are then mated (singly) to the balanced lethal (*TM3, Ser/lethal*) to determine which lines have retained the new lethal. Since not all recombinant chromosomes will retain the lethal, at least 20 of these lines must be set up.

It will usually take more than one round of free recombination to get rid of all extraneous inserts, especially if they are close to the crucial insert. For cloning purposes, it is not always necessary to eliminate all others as long as there are only a few and none are close enough to the locus in question to get confused with it when assayed by in situ hybridization. The fact that *Birm2* P-elements do not carry any special sequences to facilitate plasmid rescue means that any new insertion allele must be cloned by making a library from the mutant flies. Finally, remobilization of the insert, a key step in showing that the new mutant phenotype is indeed the result of said insertion, is much easier with a genetic marker. The advantages of using $P[w^+]$ elements are apparent.

**PROBLEM 6**    Redesign the scheme outlined above to incorporate an attached-$X,y$ chromosome with eight $P[w^+]$ elements as the source of transposons.

## Mutating Genes for Which There Are No Allelic Differences

Many genes have been identified in the fly on the basis of molecular or biochemical characterization of normal gene products for which no mutations exist. Loci for these genes have mostly been mapped by in situ hybridization to polytene chromosomes. Usually, one wants to have mutations in these genes, but this can be problematic if there is no simple way of recognizing when the locus is mutant. Unlike yeast and mice, flies do not yet seem easily amenable to gene replacement by homologous recombination. Some attempts at this have been made, but they require the pre-existing condition of two nearby P-elements (Gloor et al. 1991; Keeler et al. 1996). There have been several alternative approaches adopted to deal with this difficulty.

### Screening Over a Deletion of the Locus

The most straightforward way of finding a mutation, if you have some idea of what kind of phenotype to expect, is to obtain a deletion that uncovers the cloned locus and simply blast away at it with mutagens. A standard screen for failure to survive over the deletion will turn up all the lethals, useful if you have reason to believe that your gene can mutate to lethality. If lethality is not expected, but some tissue-specific phenotype (such as roughening of the eye, for which there appear to be a virtually unlimited number of genes in the fly), then one can focus on that tissue and its morphology. Here it becomes important what mutagen is used, since it is crucial to mutate the gene in a way that will be easily detectable at the DNA level. Radiation (see above) is preferable for this purpose.

### Insertional Mutations of Cloned Genes

One approach to obtaining mutations in cloned genes is a PCR-based technique for detecting P-element insertions into a site whose sequence is known (Ballinger and Benzer 1989; Kaiser and Goodwin 1990; Dalby et al. 1995). The genetic aspects of this scheme are just like those for generating new enhancer-trap lines and do not require any other genetic tools for analyzing the locus, such as deletions or breakpoints. Putative new insertion chromosomes are then assayed by PCR, looking for the presence of a replicated segment using one primer from the P-element flanking sequences and the other from the target genomic region. The rationale is that no such band can ever be produced unless a P-element has inserted into or near enough to the region containing the other primer sequence. Because of the sensitivity of PCR, DNA can be pooled from many such putative insertion lines for the assay.

Specifically, the following cross, using males carrying 17 defective P-elements, is performed at 16°C. The mobilization of these P-elements is induced by the stably inserted transposase $P[ry^+\Delta2\text{-}3]$ (see p. 39, above). The low temperature minimizes lethality and male sterility brought on by the hybrid dysgenesis produced by the mobilization of P-elements in the cross.

$$\text{♂♂} \quad Birm2 \quad \times \quad \frac{w}{w'} \;;\; \frac{Sb\ P[ry^+\Delta 2\text{-}3]}{TM6} \quad \text{♀♀} \qquad \text{En masse at 16°C}$$

$$\downarrow$$

$$\text{♂♂} \quad \frac{Sb\ P[ry^+\Delta 2\text{-}3]}{+} \quad \times \quad \frac{+}{+} \quad \text{♀♀} \qquad \text{En masse at 18°C}$$

$$\downarrow$$

Individual males, not $Sb$  $\quad \text{♂} \quad \dfrac{[*P]}{+} \quad \times \quad \dfrac{+}{+} \quad$  Ten ♀♀ per vial

Female progeny are then pooled from 10 vials at a time for DNA extraction and PCR analysis. PCR primers consist of two from each end of the P-element, oriented outward from the center of the P-element, and some number of primers ($\geq 2$) from sites in the gene being targeted. (Three primers restrict the possible sites of detectable insertion, reducing the probability of obtaining inserts but maximizing the reliability of the assay by eliminating interference and nonspecific priming.) Presence of an amplified band indicates presence of one or more individuals in the pool carrying an insert. Subsequent rounds of sib-selection (subdivision of the original pool of strains into smaller pools) eventually yields a strain with the desired insert. In a screen for insertions into the RI regulatory subunit of protein kinase A, Goodwin et al. (1993; S.F. Goodwin, pers. comm.) obtained 2 out of 12,000 females screened. Given the predilection of P-elements to hop to nearby sites, and the proliferation of strains with identified insertion sites, the prospects for this become more favorable all the time.

A variant of this approach that has yielded some successes makes use of P-element vectors capable of plasmid rescue (Bier et al. 1989; Wilson et al. 1989). In this scheme, such P-elements are mobilized and lines are derived carrying putative new insertions (Zinsmaier et al. 1994). DNA is then prepared from these lines and treated appropriately for plasmid rescue (digested, ligated, and transformed into *E. coli*). The transformants are then blotted and subjected to colony hybridization using a probe from the original cloned gene. This procedure increases the sensitivity of the screen.

Another variant on this technique, developed by Dalby et al. (1995), pools flies carrying new insertions and uses PCR to generate probes from the sequences flanking these insertions. These probes are then hybridized with defined genomic clones and the process is repeated for sib selection. The approach succeeded in identifying 11 hits in five genomic intervals out of 16,000 new insertions.

## Biochemical Assays for Mutations

When there is no clear basis for predicting a phenotype, it can be advantageous to assay directly for the gene product in mutagenized lines of flies. There is no selection involved here; one must assay individually each line of the thousands of mutagenized chromosomes. This is the approach used successfully to obtain mutants at the chaoptin locus, a gene whose product was originally identified by a monoclonal antibody (Van Vactor et al. 1988). A simple, solid-phase antibody assay was carried out on homogenates of fly heads from lines carrying a mutagenized chromosome over a deletion of the locus. One such mutation was found in 10,000 lines. A variation of this approach has also worked, using Western blots instead of a solid-phase assay (Dolph et al. 1993). Enzyme assays can also be used as the antibody assays described above.

If it is possible to predict the phenotype of the mutation being sought, such as lethality or eye roughening, a pre-screen can be made, consisting of all of the mutations uncovered by the relevant deletion producing that phenotype. This is usually easier than assaying each mutagenized chromosome line. The biochemical assay can then be used to pick out which one(s) is in the right gene (Greenspan 1980).

# CHAPTER 3

# Mapping

Once you have found a new mutation, you will need to know where it maps. If it has been induced in a scheme that is not directed at a particular region of the genome, you must resort to the tried and true techniques of linkage and recombinational analysis.

Linkage analysis relies on Mendel's principle of segregation of alleles—that the two homologs of a chromosome segregate reliably and inexorably from each other during the first meiotic division. Therefore, if the mutation is on the opposite homolog from a dominant marker, and if there is no recombination between the two homologs, they will segregate from each other in every meiosis and thus in all the progeny. This segregation cannot be confounded by recombination in males because they have none. In females, ambiguities due to recombination can be prevented by using balancer chromosomes.

Chromosome segregation, like all things biological, is not foolproof. Improper segregation does occur, but generally at a rate so low that it is of no consequence for our purposes. It can become significant and troublesome, however, when rearranged chromosomes are involved, such as translocations or multiple inversions. Under certain circumstances, these will not pair and segregate normally. The resulting gametes do not contain a normal genetic complement but may have too much or too little genetic material. This condition is called *aneuploidy* (as opposed to having the proper genetic complement, called *euploidy*). Since aneuploidy at the level of whole chromosomes (with the exception of chromosome 4, *XXY*, and *X0*) is lethal to embryos, occasional failures of segregation will not even be noticeable in the adult progeny that you score in your analysis.

Recombinational analysis relies on the fact that the frequency of chromosomal exchange between two loci is related to the distance between them. The recombination occurs in females who are heterozygous for your mutation and for other markers on the same chromosome. The basic analysis has not changed since its first use by Sturtevant to establish the order of genes on the $X$ chromosome of the fly in 1913. In this way, you can establish an approximate position for your gene prior to zeroing in more accurately with deletions, duplications, and breakpoints.

Mapping strategies can also be used to identify genes if there is a convenient assay for the product or for a particular phenotype. Such strategies rely on chromosomal rearrangements systematically to create deletions or duplications of regions of the genome and can serve as an efficient precursor to mutagenesis; i.e., you can often identify the general region containing a gene you want, then screen for mutations there.

## SEGREGATION ANALYSIS

Tracking a mutation by its segregation from a dominant marker is fundamental to all mating schemes in the fly. As shown previously in the discussion of mutagenesis schemes, this is what identifies unambiguously which flies are carrying recessive mutations. It requires dominant markers and balancers for the second and third chromosomes. Linkage to the $X$ is easier to see, since recessive mutations are hemizygous in males and, if introduced from a male, are only transmitted to female progeny. The fourth chromosome is usually left out of these schemes. If a mutation does not map to the $X$, second, or third, linkage to chromosome 4 can be confirmed. There are dominant markers for chromosome 4, such as the dominant alleles of eyeless $(ey^D)$ and cubitus interruptus $(ci^D)$, but no balancers, since it does not undergo exchange even in females (except in triploids).

Dominant mutations are always the easiest to map, because they can be directly scored in the next generation. One simply mates the mutant flies to a stock carrying dominant markers on one or more of the other chromosomes, selects male progeny heterozygous for all of the dominants, then mates them to a wild-type strain to score segregation in the next generation. When males are used, there is no danger that exchange will cause the mutation to become linked to one of the markers. This could become a problem if the mutation maps far from the marker for its chromosome, because loci that are distant from each other on the same chromosome will appear to assort independently, as if they were unlinked, when exchange is active. An example of a cross to test segregation of a dominant $(Dom)$ is:

$$\frac{Dom}{+} \quad \times \quad \frac{In(2LR)O,Cy}{Sco} \; ; \; \frac{TM6}{Sb}$$

$$\downarrow$$

$$\frac{Sco}{Dom?} \; ; \; \frac{Sb}{} \quad \times \quad \frac{+}{+}$$

Then score whether the new dominant segregates from $Sco$ or $Sb$

P-element insertions, either new transformants or enhancer-trap jumps, can be mapped by the same strategy, since these lines are usually marked with the wild-type alleles of rosy ($ry^+$) or white ($w^+$) and will act as dominant on a mutant background of $ry$ or $w$ (see p. 39).

$$\frac{w}{Y} \; ; \; \frac{P[w^+]}{+} \quad \times \quad \frac{w}{w} \; ; \; \frac{In(2LR)O,Cy}{Sco} \quad \text{or} \quad \frac{w}{w} \; ; \; \frac{TM3,\,Ser}{Sb}$$

$$\downarrow$$

$$\frac{w}{Y} \; ; \; \frac{In(2LR)O,Cy}{P[w^+]?} \; \; \frac{+}{} \quad \text{or} \quad \frac{w}{Y} \; ; \; \frac{+;\,TM3,\,Ser}{P[w^+]?} \quad \times \quad \frac{w}{w} \; ; \; \frac{+}{+}$$

Then score whether $w^+$
segregates from $Cy$, $Ser$,
or neither

Recessive mutations are not much more difficult to map, requiring only the generation of males and females heterozygous for both the mutation and the markers. That is, when testing for segregation of a recessive mutation, you must mate heterozygotes to reveal the presence of the mutation. This means that balancer chromosomes must be used as the source of dominant markers in the heterozygous females to prevent exchange.

## Problems with Balancers

It would be too good to be true if balancers didn't also present some problems. Although these are not all pertinent to the use of balancers for segregation analysis and meiotic mapping, and will matter more in the next chapter on Synthesizing Specific Genotypes, there is enough reason to mention them now.

One kind of problem, already alluded to, is the probability (albeit low) of a recombination event causing breakdown of a balancer. For this reason, it is wise when keeping and using balanced stocks to check routinely for whether all the flies have the markers they are supposed to have. This simple bit of compulsiveness can save a great deal of time and trouble by allowing the detection of such an event before it takes over the stock. The best way to deal with the discovery of an inappropriate fly is to discard that particular bottle or vial if there are other copies that show correct markers, or to start several new lines from single pairs of males and virgin females carrying the appropriate markers.

A more common problem occurs when a cross requires the generation of flies carrying balancers for two different chromosomes. Females heterozygous for two different balancers produce far fewer viable offspring than females carrying only one. This is due to the dependence of chromosome segregation at meiosis on exchange between homologs. When no rearrangements are present, the vast majority of X-chromosome and all of the second and third chromosome homologs recombine during female meiosis. When one copy of an inversion chromosome is present, it too still segregates correctly from its homolog; but when two different chromosomes have heterozygous inversions, segregation runs amok. Exchange is prevented and they pair inappropriately. The result is that the wrong chromosomes segregate from each other (e.g., a second chromosome can segregate from a third chromosome or an X from a second chromosome) to produce aneuploid gametes and dead embryos.

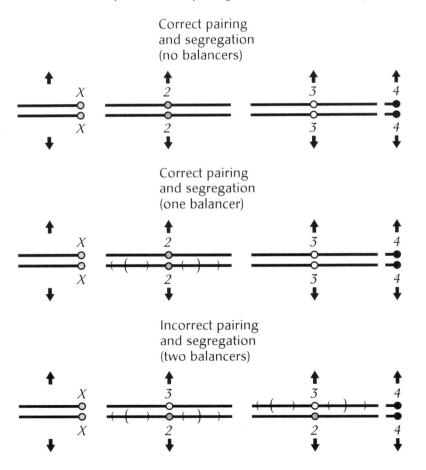

An attached-$X$ in the same stock with a second or third chromosome balancer will have the same problem of incorrect pairing and segregation. Males, in contrast, do not have such problems. Even in the presence of multiple balancer chromosomes, segregation occurs normally.

A secondary difficulty that surfaces when multiple, heterozygous inversions are present in the same stock is that the likelihood of balancer breakdown increases. This is due to another anomaly, called the interchromosomal effect, in which the heterozygous rearrangements suppress exchange in part of the genome, increasing the likelihood of recombination occurring elsewhere. Thus, the presence of one balancer increases the probability of a rare breakdown event in another balancer. Although not nearly as common a problem as the incorrect segregation described above, this can still be an annoyance. It becomes more than an annoyance when mapping a new mutation meiotically, as it distorts the map distances and accentuates the chances of otherwise rare exchange events.

The remedy for these problems is to anticipate that crosses involving females with two balancers will go poorly and to try to circumvent them in the design of the mating scheme. The easiest way to do this is to transmit the two balancers through males, since they segregate chromosomes perfectly well regardless of the presence of inversions. If there is no alternative, use many more flies than you would normally and keep a sharp eye out for balancer breakdowns in the progeny.

## MEIOTIC MAPPING

Once the linkage of a new mutation is known, the most efficient way to find its location on the chromosome, in the absence of cloned pieces or sequence information, is to map it by recombinational analysis. This generally involves a multiply marked chromosome, whose mutations lie at intervals along the chromosome, and a similar chromosome that also carries a dominant marker. The basic strategy is to generate females heterozygous for the chromosome bearing the new mutation and for the marker chromosome. These will recombine during meiosis, and the various classes of recombinant chromosomes, produced in proportion to the distance between markers and mutation, will go into her eggs.

The task is then to measure the proportion of different recombinant chromosomes and thus determine the position of the new mutation relative to the markers. To obtain a preliminary map interval, it is easiest to cross the heterozygous female to another version of the marker chromosome— one that contains a dominant marker as well. Then, males carrying recombinant chromosomes can be recognized and picked up as heterozygotes for the dominant marker. Whether a male has a particular recombinant interval can easily be scored by how many of the recessive markers are now homozygous. These males are then mated individually to the original stock carrying the lethal mutation to assess the presence of the lethal on the recombinant chromosome.

A simple mapping scheme for a new, recessive lethal $(\ell)$ on the third chromosome uses a multiply marked chromosome known affectionately as "rucuca" which carries roughoid (ru) 3-0.0, hairy (h) 3-26.5, thread (th) 3-43.2, scarlet (st) 3-44.0, curled (cu) 3-50.0, striped (sr) 3-62.0, ebony (e) 3-70.7, and claret (ca) 3-100.7, and its cognate chromosome "ruPrica" which also has the dominant marker Prickly (Pr) 3-90.0:

$$\frac{TM6,\ Ubx}{\ell} \quad \times \quad \frac{ru\ cu\ ca}{ru\ cu\ ca} \qquad \textbf{P}$$

Essential to collect females ♀♀ $\dfrac{ru\ cu\ ca}{\ell}$ × $\dfrac{ruPrica}{+}$ ♂♂ **F1**
heterozygous for $\ell$ and markers.

Select males heterozygous for ruPrica and with cross-overs in each interval, recognizable by homozygosity of appropriate markers, and cross individually to original lethal-bearing chromosome

$$\frac{ru\ (\ell?)\ +}{ruPrica} \qquad \frac{ru\ h\ th\ st\ cu\ (\ell?)\ +}{ruPrica}$$

$$\frac{ru\ h\ (\ell?)\ +}{ruPrica} \qquad \frac{ru\ h\ th\ st\ cu\ sr\ (\ell?)\ +}{ruPrica}$$

♂  ×  $\dfrac{TM6,\ Ubx}{\ell}$  ♀♀  **F2**

$$\frac{ru\ h\ th\ (\ell?)\ +}{ruPrica} \qquad \frac{ru\ h\ th\ st\ cu\ sr\ e\ (\ell?)\ +}{ruPrica}$$

$$\frac{ru\ h\ th\ st\ (\ell?)\ +}{ruPrica} \qquad \frac{ru\ h\ th\ st\ cu\ sr\ e\ ca\ (\ell?)}{ruPrica}$$

Score progeny for absence of Ubx and Pr, indicative of the presence of the lethal on the recombinant chromosome

(These hypothetical recombinant chromosomes are drawn to reflect single cross-over events. In reality, many would have double cross-overs [e.g., *ru h + + + sr e ca*] but could still serve your purposes.)

This analysis defines the chromosomal interval in which the new mutation lies and can be accomplished with a few flies of each genotype. Finer grain localization can then be carried out either by deletion mapping with available deficiencies of the region or by collecting many recombinants between the two markers in an interval and scoring the actual percentage of cross-overs separating the *lethal* from one versus the other.

Map positions, as reported in Lindsley and Zimm (1992), are denoted by the chromosome followed by a normalized value for the meiotic map position, e.g., (2-36.8). The normalization is an attempt to order the genes on the chromosome in an approximate fashion by adding map values from left tip to right tip of the chromosome. Thus, it is possible for a locus to have a map position of greater than 50 map units, even though no one could ever measure a value greater than 50 in a single mapping experiment. These numbers, and the gene order derived from them, are to be taken and used with caution. Direct mapping between specific loci is the only way to obtain reliable results. Meiotic map positions are standardly measured using heterozygous females that have been raised at 25°C. This is because recombination frequency is sensitive to temperature (Ashburner 1989).

Some of the value of traditional meiotic map positions has diminished as the molecular mapping of the fly genome has progressed with its correlation of loci with sequences. The persisting value of meiotic mapping lies in the narrowing down of a new mutation's position from that of the whole chromosome to a rough interval and in the demonstration that a phenotype is due to a single gene. This can be readily accomplished by using a few markers and obtaining a relative map. Once the interval is known, a finer localization can be obtained with deletions or with marked P-element insertions mapped to the region.

An important issue to bear in mind is that the markers should not interfere with the phenotype of the new mutation. If the new mutation causes an embryonic pattern defect that can be scored in an individual offspring, there will be little danger of interference from markers. If, on the other hand, scoring requires a population of flies of like genotype (e.g., for a behavior mutant), there could be significant trouble due to marker phenotypes that blur the distinction between behavioral mutant and wild type. In such a case, using a hypothetical example on chromosome *2*, one might set up crosses that test for the presence of two benign markers (straw, *stw*, 2-55.1 for bristle color and brown, *bw*, 2-104.5 for eye color) and generate the population of flies to be tested for the new mutation (*n*) in parallel:

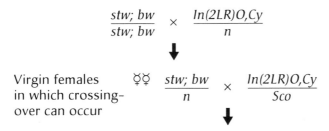

Virgin females
in which crossing–
over can occur

$$\frac{stw;\ bw}{n} \times \frac{In(2LR)O,Cy}{Sco}$$

Collect males heterozygous for either *In(2LR)O,Cy* or *Sco*, who will carry potentially recombinant chromosomes, and mate them individually in vials to a mixture of two types of females

| $\frac{stw;\ bw}{stw;\ bw}$ | | $\frac{In(2LR)O,Cy\ or\ Sco}{?\ n\ ?}$ | | $\frac{In(2LR)O,Cy}{n}$ |
|---|---|---|---|---|
| ♀♀ | | Single ♂ | | ♀♀ |

After a suitable mating period (5–7 days), place the two types of females into separate vials and score progeny

What markers            Is *n* present?
are present?

The relative proportion of lines that have *stw* with *n*, *bw* with *n*, both with *n*, and neither with *n*, will tell which marker *n* is closer to and whether it is between them or outside of them. (The closer *n* is to a marker locus, the less often will recombination occur between them and the more often will *n* segregate with the allele [marker⁺ in this case] to which it was originally linked.)

**PROBLEM 7** Assume you have just isolated a new, viable learning mutation on an *X* chromosome already carrying vermilion *(v)* at 1–33.0. Design a scheme for mapping the new mutation relative to *v* and to yellow *(y)* at 1–0.0 and forked *(f)* at 1-56.7.

| *y* | *v* | *f* |
|---|---|---|

Relative positions of *y, v,* and *f*

## DELETION MAPPING

Once the approximate location of a mutation is known from meiotic mapping, a more accurate placement can often be assigned by testing various chromosome deletions for their ability to uncover a recessive mutant phenotype. When a mutation is caused by an insertion element, concordance of the mutant phenotype with the site of insertion can be tested most rapidly by deletion mapping. The smaller the deletion, the more accurate the localization down to the limiting case of a chromosomal breakpoint.

This kind of mapping is indistinguishable from a complementation test in which one is testing for the failure of complementation between a deletion and a mutation (see Chapter 2). After testing a variety of deletions for a given region, the gene can be localized to the shortest interval between the available breakpoints.

Most deletions have been induced by radiation. Some result from chemical mutagenesis (e.g., EMS), and an increasing number are being created by imprecise P-element excisions. These latter excision-generated deletions are often (but by no means always) small, generally not affecting more than one locus or its immediate neighbor. They are listed in Lindsley and Zimm (1992) and in the updated computerized FlyBase (see Appendix).

For those regions of the genome that cannot be conveniently tested with existing deletions, it is possible to synthesize a deletion using chromosome rearrangements specifically designed for the purpose (see section below on Synthesis of Deletions and Duplications). Alternatively, it is also possible to generate new deletions by the technique of imprecise P-element excision (see section on Inducing Deletions in Chapter 4).

## DUPLICATION MAPPING

Precise localization of a locus can make use of any kind of chromosome aberration to bracket the gene between known breakpoints. Duplications serve this purpose when a recessive phenotype can be covered (i.e., rescued) by the presence of a duplication carrying the wild-type locus. Duplications are often the reciprocal products of the radiation events that produce deletions: A chunk of chromosome is chopped out and re-inserted elsewhere.

Since a test of rescue by a duplication requires introducing three components, the two mutant alleles and the duplication, it is desirable to use duplications in which the insertion has gone into a different chromosome. An illustration of such a test is shown below for a second-chromosome lethal ($\ell$) mutation with a duplication of the segment containing the wild-type engrailed locus inserted into the third chromosome:

$$\sigma\sigma \quad \frac{In(2LR)O,Cy}{\ell}, \frac{Dp(2;3)\ en^+}{Sb} \quad \times \quad \frac{In(2LR)O,Cy}{\ell} \quad \female\female$$

See if there are any
$Cy^+, Sb^+$ flies in the progeny
$$\frac{\ell}{\ell}, \frac{Dp(2;3)\ bw^+}{+} \quad ??$$

If there are, this indicates that $Dp(2;3)\ en^+$ covers the lethality of $\ell$. This localizes the mutation inside the breakpoints of the duplication. The approach is not foolproof, however, if a second lethal had by chance been induced on the same chromosome. A duplication capable of rescuing one lethal would not rescue the other, producing a false negative. To circumvent this problem, one can use a different, independently isolated allele of the gene if it exists, since it would never have the same two random lethals induced. (See Chapter 4 for techniques to synthesize strains.)

## SYNTHESIS OF DELETIONS AND DUPLICATIONS

Not all regions of the genome are represented by existing deletions and duplications. Those that are can be obtained as a kit from the Drosophila Stock Center at Bloomington, Indiana (see Appendix). If you are stuck with solving the problem yourself, strains were constructed by Lindsley et al. (1972) to permit synthesis of duplications almost at will and, to a lesser extent, deletions. These strains are translocations between either the second or third chromosome and a $Y$ chromosome marked with $y^+$ (the wild-type allele of yellow body color) and $B^s$ (an allele of the dominant eye mutation Bar of Stone) known as $T(Y;A)$s. Each translocation has the general structure:

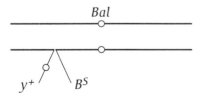

in which there is a reciprocal translocation between marked $Y$ and autosome such that each piece of the broken autosome has a different $Y$-linked marker and a centromere. (Chromosome fragments have no future if they don't have centromeres.) The entire autosome is present, but it is now broken into two pieces. These are balanced by an appropriate autosomal balancer chromosome (*Bal*). By choosing two *T(Y;A)*s with relatively nearby breakpoints and with opposite configurations of $y^+$ and $B^s$,

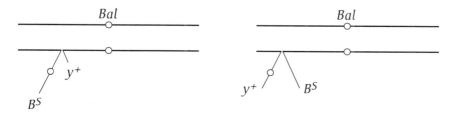

one class of progeny is produced that gets the short end of the translocations, producing a deletion; another class gets the long ends, producing a duplication; and all the others are euploid (normal amount of genetic material).

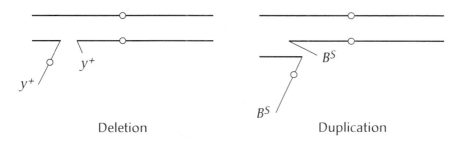

Deletion                    Duplication

The deletion is uniquely marked with two doses of $y^+$ but not $B^s$, whereas the duplication is unique with two doses of $B^s$ and none of $y^+$. The aneuploid (deleted or duplicated) progeny are a small fraction of the total progeny at best, and reduced viability associated with aneuploidy can decrease the recovery even further. An analogous set of translocations between the *X* and the same marked *Y* were generated by Stewart and Merriam (1973) and are known as *T(X;Y)*s.

The initial study for which these rearrangements were made surveyed the "gross structure" of the *Drosophila* genome (Lindsley et al. 1972) and defined several haplo-lethal loci (lethal when present as a heterozygous deletion), one of which is also triplo-lethal (lethal when duplicated). In general, they found that heterozygous deletions larger than one numbered region and duplications larger than four or five numbered regions were lethal. These are only averages, however, and there are examples of very large duplications (e.g., the entire left arm of chromosome *2*) and deletions (e.g., 37B–40B) that are viable.

In the paleolithic age prior to cloning, these stocks were successfully used to identify structural loci for several enzymes of neurobiological interest by "dosage effects." The strategy relied on the fact that duplications and deletions of these loci were not dosage compensated. That is, flies with a duplicated enzyme locus would have roughly 1.5 times as much enzyme as a normal, euploid fly. Those that were heterozygous for a deletion would have roughly 0.5 as much as euploids. (In reality, the values are quite variable and average 1.3 for duplications and 0.6 for deletions.) Crosses of 30 *T(Y;A)*s produce a series of contiguous duplications for chromosomes *2* and *3*. Crosses of two appropriately chosen *T(X;Y)*s are sufficient to produce duplications for each half of the *X*. The fourth chromosome can be tested in one cross between a stock carrying an attached-*4*, *C(4)RM*, and a stock homozygous for a fourth-chromosome marker (e.g., eyeless, *ey*) produces progeny that are either triplo-*4* or haplo-*4*.

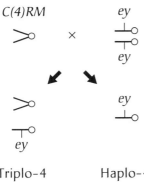

Half of the progeny will have three copies of chromosome *4* and half will have one copy. Those with three copies will look wild-type, those with one copy will look eyeless (*ey*), due to hemizygosity for the mutation, and Minute (*M*), a phenotype characterized by thin bristles and retarded development, due to hemizygosity for the Minute locus on chromosome *4* (see Chapter 4 for discussion of Minutes)

In this fashion, loci for acetylcholinesterase (Hall and Kankel 1976), dopa decarboxylase (Hodgetts 1975), cAMP phosphodiesterase (Kiger and Golanty 1977), and choline acetyltransferase (Greenspan 1980) were initially found. It was because of this cytological localization of cAMP phosphodiesterase that the molecular identity of the learning mutant dunce was solved, based on the initial realization that they mapped to the same place (Byers et al. 1981; story recounted in Greenspan 1990).

When using these stocks, it is best to carry out a series of pilot crosses (a vial or two) to make certain they are behaving as they should. This is much easier than making chromosome squashes from each. Y-autosomal breakpoints are difficult to score. The markers indicating duplication and deletion progeny are one indicator. If the two strains in the cross have breakpoints that are nowhere near each other, no duplication or deletion progeny will be produced. If they are several numbered regions apart, duplications should survive but not deletions, and so on. A more detailed characterization involves scoring the proportion of duplication progeny that are male versus female (Lindsley et al. 1972; Ashburner 1989).

To figure out which markers should indicate duplication and which deletion, one need only consult the list of these stocks to see which arm of the Y chromosome is broken in the translocation, either the short arm ($Y^S$) or the long arm ($Y^L$). In the original Y chromosome, $B^s$ was on $Y^L$ and $y^+$ on $Y^S$:

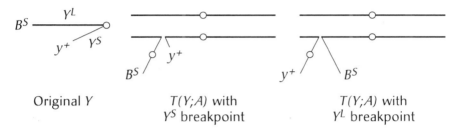

| Original Y | T(Y;A) with $Y^S$ breakpoint | T(Y;A) with $Y^L$ breakpoint |

The attrition of these stocks over the years has been significant, but many still remain. Some have lost the $B^s$ marker, but this is not always a problem if one of the two strains retains it.

PROBLEM 7    Determine what classes of progeny you could distinguish if you mated two T(Y;A)s, both of which have breakpoints in $Y^S$. Determine what classes of progeny you could distinguish if you mated two T(Y;A)s, one of which has a breakpoint in $Y^S$ and one of which has a breakpoint in $Y^L$ but has lost its $B^s$ marker.

The strength of this technique for adult flies is obvious. For embryos and larvae, on the other hand, $B^s$ is completely unrecognizable and $y^+$ is scorable only in third-instar larval mouth parts and setae (tiny hairs). It is thus not possible to know which progeny are duplicated or deleted for the segment at these pre-adult stages. This precludes most kinds of analysis except for those in which one needs only to see a distinctive phenotype in some fraction of the progeny, as in the identification of new loci.

## Identification of New Embryonic Genes by Deletion Mapping

Most deletions are homozygous lethal. This severely limits their utility for identifying new loci based on phenotype unless the phenotype can be scored at the lethal stage. For embryonic development, this is quite feasible, and a variety of new loci have been identified starting from a morphological defect in 25% of the progeny of a strain heterozygous for a deletion, or in the aneuploid progeny of a $T(X;Y)$. Even when multiple genes are deleted, as is virtually always the case, the lethal phenotype is predominantly caused by a single, early-acting gene. This is ultimately sorted out by isolating individual mutations in the deleted region (see Chapter 2) and seeing which, if any, recapitulate the phenotype of the homozygous deletion. One is limited only by the ability to screen for morphological aberrations.

The single-minded (*sim*) locus was identified in this fashion, starting from a screen of embryos from heterozygous stocks of autosomal deletions. Dead embryos were stained and examined in whole mounts. Aberrations of the ventral nerve cord were found in homozyotes for a 14-band deletion $Df(3R)$ $ry^{619}$ (Thomas et al. 1988). EMS mutagenesis and a screen for lethal mutations uncovered by this deficiency confirmed that this phenotype was due to a single gene defect.

More dramatically, one of the earliest-acting zygotic genes was identified through deletion mapping as being predominantly responsible for the phenotype produced in an embryo having no $X$ chromosome (nullo-$X$). Nullo-$X$ embryos have long been known to arrest development very early with no cellularization at blastoderm stage (Poulson 1940). This was always assumed to be a "syndrome" due to the loss of 1/5 of the genome. Wieschaus and Sweeton (1988) created large deletions of the $X$ to define the region responsible for this phenotype. They mated $T(X;Y)$ males to attached-$X$ females (each with its own intact $Y$) and cleverly scored which portion of the $X$ an embryo received by the presence or absence of the folded-gastrulation (*fog*) phenotype. *fog⁻* embryos fail to form a posterior midgut and so are easily recognized.

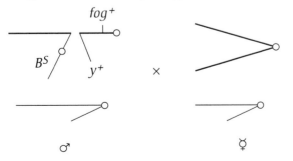

Those embryos receiving the *Y* from their mothers and a fragment of the *T(X;Y)* from their fathers will have large deletions of the *X*, distinguishable by the presence or absence of the posterior invagination induced by *fog⁺* activity. After obtaining a rough localization by this method, these investigators zeroed in on the locus by means of careful deletion mapping of the embryronic phenotype. This revealed, contrary to previous expectation, that a single, two-band region was responsible for the nullo-*X* phenotype of failed cellularization. The nullo locus was ultimately identified as the culprit (Rose and Wieschaus 1992).

Taking this approach to the autosomes, Merrill et al. (1988) utilized a different set of chromosome rearrangements to produce complete or partial deletions of autosomal arms. They used compound autosome stocks in which the two left arms are attached to a common centromere and the two right arms are attached to a common centromere. In most stocks of this sort, each set of compound arms is also homozygous for a recessive marker for ease of determining if the stock is uncontaminated (see p. 11).

When males and females of this stock are mated, some will lack *2L* and others will lack *2R*. (Segregation of these compound autosomes in males occurs randomly, whereas in females the *2L* will segregate regularly from the *2R*. Thus, males will produce gametes containing random mixtures of the various chromosome rearrangements, whereas females will produce gametes that contain one or the other.) A similar stock exists for the third chromosome. To monitor the frequency of the various classes of segregants in these stocks, they were crossed to embryonic cuticle pattern mutants located on each arm.

From this analysis, Merrill et al. (1988) were able to determine which chromosome arms carried genes that acted prior to gastrulation, similar to the *nullo-X* locus previously identified. By combining various *T(X;Y)*s with the *C(2L;2R)* stock, they were able to create smaller deletions of the appropriate arms.

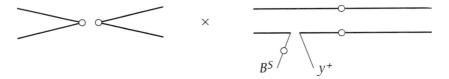

A small fraction of the progeny embryos from this cross will be totally deleted for the distal left arm:

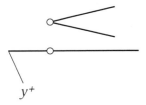

$y^+$

This analysis identified seven new loci with developmental defects preceding gastrulation, two of which affected cellularization.

Compound chromosomes of this sort are produced by radiation. To introduce recessive markers onto their arms, which is essential for knowing what you have, one produces triploid females in which the one normal set of chromosomes carries the desired recessive mutations, $m_1$, $m_2$, $m_3$, $m_4$, and $m_5$ (e.g., Hardy 1975):

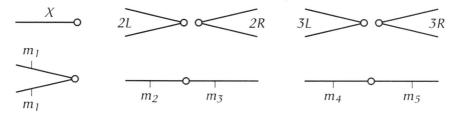

## MAPPING BY IN SITU HYBRIDIZATION

A technique that has become as standard as linkage analysis for mapping insertion sites of P-elements is in situ hybridization. It represents the fastest and most direct way to localize a new insertion site. However, a mutant phenotype must be independently mapped to the site of a new insertion, either by excision, deletion, or recombination analysis. Techniques for in situ hybridization are described in Ashburner (1989).

Cytological positions obtained from in situ hybridization (or from analysis of chromosome breakpoints) are expressed as "band numbers" in reference to the chromosome bands visible in preparations of larval salivary gland chromosomes (see p. 6).

The correspondence between meiotic map positions and cytological band positions is not a simple one, varying with position along the chromosome. Specific correlations can be found (or guessed at) in the computerized listing of FlyBase.

# CHAPTER 4

# Synthesizing Specific Genotypes

Virtuoso fly genetics reaches its pinnacle with the art of synthesizing strains and generating new rearrangements. The Stradivarius of this art, Ed Novitski, set a standard that has yet to be equalled with his synthesis of an entire, diploid set of autosomes attached to a single centromere. Not surprisingly, meiotic segregation was not a happy event in this strain and it did not survive very well, but the principle was established.

For most purposes, the extent of complex stock construction only goes as far as putting a few chromosomes together in the same fly. This can be more complicated than it sounds and always requires some planning. Many are the times when I thought I could whip off a new strain in a few crosses starting from stocks I happened to have handy, only to find two generations later that I couldn't distinguish genotypes clearly and had to start over again doing it the right way.

The ability to distinguish genotypes unambiguously is the heart and soul of fly chromosome manipulation. It is the feature that sets fly genetics apart from all others and that is essential to exploiting the full potential of the organism.

## Principles

The strategies for stock construction take advantage of the following facts, most of which have been said before but which bear repeating:

1. Homologous chromosomes segregate from each other reliably during meiosis; thus, if a progeny received a particular chromosome from its mother, it did not also receive that chromosome's homolog.
2. There are dominant markers and balancers for each of the chromosomes; this tells which homolog from each parent a progeny received, either by presence of the marker or by its absence (see 1 above).
3. There is no recombination in males and a balancer chromosome effec-

tively suppresses recombination with its homolog in females; this means that a dominant marker that starts out on a particular homolog will stay on that homolog through meiosis and thus serve as a reliable marker for it.

As a result of these facts, all chromosomes can be faithfully followed.

Designing schemes for fly matings is a little like doing problems in organic chemistry. You have to figure out how to combine the available starting materials in the most economical and reliable steps to reach a final product, and you have to be able to "purify" the product of each step before proceeding with the next. It is often helpful to work backward from the final product. (If the organic chemistry analogy summons up bad memories, don't worry; fly mating schemes are more fun and ultimately more satsifying to carry out. In addition, you can work on them while sitting in boring seminars or lab meetings.)

## SIMPLE MANIPULATIONS OF A SINGLE CHROMOSOME

This is the baseline of fly manipulations and is essentially the same as outlined in Chapter 2 on isolating mutants and performing complementation tests. The principle of identifying progeny by absence of dominant markers is illustrated in this complementation test between hunchback (*hb*) and a new third-chromosome lethal:

$$\frac{TM3, Ser}{\ell} \times \frac{TM6, Ubx}{hb}$$

$$\downarrow$$

$\frac{\ell}{hb}$    Survival of this class of progeny that are
         non-*Ubx* and non-*Ser* indicates complementation

The key feature of this cross is that each genotype is distinguished by a unique combination of markers—a goal to be aspired to always.

### Linking Mutations

Another common manipulation, slightly more involved, is recombining two mutations (or a P-element insertion and a mutation) onto the same chromosome. This is often necessary for carrying out double mutant tests (see Chapter 5) and for linking markers to mutations for mosaic analysis (see Chapter 6).

In its simplest form, the process requires females that are doubly heterozygous on the same chromosome for the two mutations to be linked.

One then recovers individual, putative recombinant chromosomes in the progeny of these females and tests them for the presence of both mutations. An example is shown below for making a double mutant of odd-skipped and even-skipped on the second chromosome:

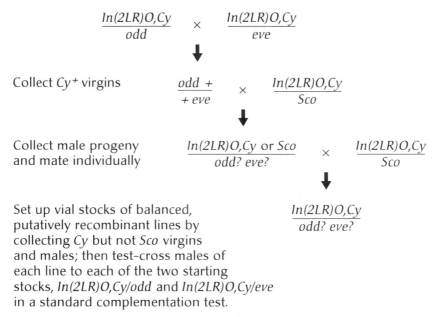

Collect *Cy*⁺ virgins

Collect male progeny
and mate individually

Set up vial stocks of balanced,
putatively recombinant lines by
collecting *Cy* but not *Sco* virgins
and males; then test-cross males of
each line to each of the two starting
stocks, *In(2LR)O,Cy/odd* and *In(2LR)O,Cy/eve*
in a standard complementation test.

The question immediately comes up of how many vial stocks to set up of putatively recombinant chromosomes. The answer is, it depends on how far apart the two mutations are. The farther apart, the more likely you are to recover the product you want. In this case, *odd* and *eve* are very far apart, approximately 50 map units, which is equivalent to being unlinked. Therefore, you will probably get it in 10 lines, but ought to do 20 just in case.

For loci that are closer together, you need to use correspondingly higher numbers of lines to be certain of recovering your recombinant. The expectation is a simple function of map distance: If there are 5 map units between loci, there is a 5% chance of recombination. You might recover it in 100 lines, but would be better advised to do 200.

(To be more rational about this, you can use Mather's [1951] formula for calculating how many progeny [*N*] you need for a 95% probability [*p*] of obtaining a recombinant if *f* is the expected fraction of progeny that will be recombinant:

$N = -\log (1-p)/\log(1-f)$

If the expected recombination frequency is 1%, to be 95% certain of obtaining the desired recombinant, you need to score ~300 progeny.)

As mentioned earlier, exchange is temperature-sensitive. Both high and low temperatures increase it (go figure!), so the probability of obtaining a recombinant chromosome for two closely linked markers can be somewhat increased (~twofold) by raising the doubly heterozygous females at 30°C (Plough 1917). It is crucial that these double heterozygotes are *raised* at high temperature, rather than simply placed there as adults for the next cross, because the critical period for this effect does not extend into adulthood. On the other hand, if they are raised at 30°C for their entire life cycle, their fecundity (egg-laying) will be reduced by approximately twofold. Therefore, the best compromise is to shift the bottles to 30°C for most of the larval period—that is, beginning when you see the food starting to be churned up and ending when you see pupae beginning to form on the sides of the bottle. The high-temperature effect is most pronounced near the centromere and the tips of the chromosome arms.

Another condition that will increase recombination is the presence of a heterozygous inversion on another chromosome. This "interchromosomal effect" increases recombination anywhere in the genome outside of the rearranged regions.

> **PROBLEM 8**   Work out how to recombine a *P[w+lacZ]* insertion element located on 3L in cytological region 61B (meiotic map position approximately 3-0) with a mutation at the hairy (*h*) locus (3-26.5).

Sometimes it helps to use additional, visible markers to aid in the recognition of recombinants for invisible, recessive mutations. This is very easy to do if, for instance, you have carried out meiotic mapping of your mutation and therefore already have a chromosome with your invisible mutation and some visible markers on it.

## MANIPULATING TWO CHROMOSOMES

To control the genotype on two different chromosomes at once, it is necessary to start planning the mating schemes. Here we will make use of balancers, dominant markers, the lack of recombination in males, and the reliable segregation of homologs. As an example, we'll consider how to make a stock to produce double mutant embryos for *ftz* on the third chromosome and *eve* on the second chromosome.

Most mutation-bearing stocks contain the mutation and a balancer for that chromosome, e.g., *TM3, Ser/ftz*. This is the healthiest way to keep them, since the presence of other dominant markers and balancers on other chromosomes only detracts from the stock's viability. To manipulate two chromosomes at once, it is necessary to introduce additional balancers and dominants, but to do so without losing track of the original chromosome. For this reason, it is useful to keep on hand a stock with two chromosomes'-worth of balancers and markers, such as:

$$FM7a; \frac{TM6, Ubx}{Sb} \text{ or } \frac{In(2LR)O, Cy}{Sco} ; \frac{TM3, Ser}{Sb} \text{ or } \frac{In(2LR)O, CyO}{Sco} ; \frac{TM6, Ubx}{Sb}$$

However, the deleterious effects of multiple balancers on female meiosis indicate that males of these genotypes should be used whenever possible. The trick is to mate the starting mutant stock with another that uses different markers. That way, one can exploit the obligatory segregation of homologs to trade markers:

### Cross #1

$$♀♀ \; \frac{TM6, Ubx}{ftz} \quad \times \quad \frac{In(2LR)O, Cy}{Sco} ; \frac{TM3, Ser}{Sb} \; ♂♂$$

$$\downarrow$$

**F1**   ♀♀   $\dfrac{In(2LR)O, Cy}{+} ; \dfrac{TM3, Ser}{ftz}$    *ftz* is now recoverable in the same flies with the balancer *In(2LR)O,Cy* in the *Ser, Ubx+* progeny. These are not particularly healthy and happy females, however, due to the presence of two balancers.

In this first step, you build out from one chromosome onto another.

In parallel, make an analogous genotype from the other mutant line:

### Cross #2

$$♀♀ \; \frac{In(2LR)O, Cy}{eve} \quad \times \quad \frac{In(2LR)O, Cy}{Sco} ; \frac{TM6, Ubx}{Sb} \; ♂♂$$

$$\downarrow$$

**F1**   ♂♂   $\dfrac{Sco}{eve} ; \dfrac{TM6, Ubx}{+}$    *eve* is now recoverable heterozygous with the dominant *Sco* in the same flies with the balancer *TM6, Ubx* in the *Sco, Cy+* males. The flies of this genotype that are used in any ubsequent cross must be males, however, to prevent any exchange on the second chromosome that could put *eve* and *Sco* on the same homolog.

Now the F1 virgins from Cross #1 and the F1 males from Cross #2 can be mated to yield a stock for producing double mutants:

$$\text{♀♀} \quad \frac{In(2LR)O,Cy}{+} \; ; \; \frac{TM3, Ser}{ftz} \quad \times \quad \frac{Sco}{eve} \; ; \; \frac{TM6, Ubx}{+} \quad \text{♂♂}$$

$$\downarrow$$

$$\frac{In(2LR)O,Cy}{eve} \; ; \; \frac{TM6, Ubx}{ftz}$$

Collected as males and virgin females ($Cy$, $Sco^+$ and $Ubx$, $Ser^+$), these flies will constitute a true-breeding (albeit unhealthy) stock, 1/16 of whose progeny would be doubly homozygous for *eve* and *ftz*. If, perchance, this *eve* mutation suppressed the lethality of this *ftz* mutation (see Chapter 5), even if only 1% of the time, it could be detected and scored unambiguously by the markers in this stock. A unique combination of markers permits each genotype to be distinguished at each step.

If, on the other hand, all you wanted to do was produce doubly mutant embryos, these adult markers would be useless, and the desired result could have been obtained much more simply and with better viability by crossing the two original stocks:

$$\frac{In(2LR)O,Cy}{eve} \; ; \; \frac{+}{+} \quad \times \quad \frac{+}{+} \; ; \; \frac{TM6, Ubx}{ftz}$$

$$\downarrow$$

$$\frac{eve}{+} \; ; \; \frac{ftz}{+}$$

Collect $Cy^+$, $Ubx^+$ males and virgins, mate them to each other and collect embryos, 25% of which will be doubly homozygous for *eve* and *ftz*

The drawback of this simple approach is that there is no way of knowing if the double mutant phenotype is different from either of the single mutant phenotypes. To solve this problem, one makes use of balancer chromosomes that have P-elements expressing *lacZ* in them. Then, when progeny are collected from the stock consisting of *In(2LR)O,Cy P[lacZ]/eve; TM6, Ubx P[lacZ]/ftz*, they can be stained for β-galactosidase. Only those progeny failing to stain will be double mutants.

The value of markers becomes apparent whenever you want to score viability, detect small numbers of progeny of a given genotype, and recover individual progeny of known genotype.

An additional tool that is helpful for manipulating the second and third chromosomes simultaneously is a reciprocal translocation between *In(2LR)O,Cy* and *TM9* called *T(2;3) CyO; TM9*. As a reciprocal translocation between both balancers, it ensures that all pieces of the translocation must be present in a fertilized egg for it to be viable—if not, the zygote will be aneuploid and will die. Since it contains complete sequences for both chromosomes, it effectively balances all of chromosomes 2 and 3 and allows one to keep a stock such as:

$$\frac{T(2;3)\ CyO;\ TM9}{eve;\ ftz}$$

Manipulations of two chromosomes are necessary when producing P-element transformants to see if a genomic clone rescues a mutant phenotype. Then you can use the visible marker in the P-element (e.g., $w^+$) as a dominant marker, provided the X chromosomes in the scheme all carry a mutant allele of white.

For example, if you have produced a transformed line carrying a $P[w^+, odd^+]$ insert on the third chromosome and you want to construct flies that are homozygous for *odd* on the second chromosome and also carry this P-element on their third chromosome, it helps to start with stocks that are mutant for *w*. This will generally be true already of the P-element-containing stock, since it will probably have been made with *w* in it:

$$w;\ \frac{P[w^+,\ odd^+]}{+}\quad \text{but will need to be made for } odd \quad w;\ \frac{In(2LR)O,Cy}{odd}$$

Similarly, all the balancer stocks used in the scheme must be *w*. These are stocks that one would generally have on hand anyway to do linkage analysis of newly derived transformants (see Chapter 3).

Since $P[w^+, odd^+]$ will be scorable as dominant on a *w* background, the scheme is somewhat simpler than the previous example for making a double mutant:

$$
\begin{array}{ccc}
\textbf{Cross \#1} & & \textbf{Cross \#2} \\
\text{♀♀} & & \text{♂♂} \qquad\qquad \text{♀♀} \\
\dfrac{w}{w'}\cdot\dfrac{P[w^+,\,odd^+]}{+} \;\times\; \dfrac{w}{Y'}\cdot\dfrac{In(2LR)O,Cy}{Sco} & \;\times\; & \dfrac{In(2LR)O,Cy}{odd} \quad \textbf{P}
\end{array}
$$

Select $w^+\ Cy\ Sco^+$
virgins from ♀♀ $\dfrac{w}{w'}\cdot\dfrac{In(2LR)O,Cy}{+}\;;\;\dfrac{P[w^+,\,odd^+]}{+}\;\times\;\dfrac{w}{Y'}\cdot\dfrac{Sco}{odd}$ ♂♂ **F1**
Cross #1 and
$Sco\ Cy^+$ males
from Cross #2

Select $w^+\ Cy\ Sco^+$
virgins and males

$$
\dfrac{w}{Y'}\cdot\dfrac{In(2LR)O,Cy}{odd}\;;\;\dfrac{P[w^+,\,odd^+]}{+}\;\times\;\dfrac{w}{w'}\cdot\dfrac{In(2LR)O,Cy}{odd}\;;\;\dfrac{P[w^+,\,odd^+]}{+}\quad \textbf{F2}
$$

See if there are any $\quad\dfrac{w}{Y}$ or $\dfrac{w}{w'}\cdot\dfrac{odd}{odd}\;;\;\dfrac{P[w^+,\,odd^+]}{+}$ **F3**
$w^+\ Cy^+$ adults

The first line of this scheme is shorthand for the fact that two crosses were set up separately but simultaneously in the parental (P) generation, using males of the same genotype for each. The last line shows that you get both males ($w/Y$) and females ($w/w$) that test the efficacy of the P-element rescue. If $odd/odd$; $P[w^+,\,odd^+]/+$ flies survive, the insert rescues the mutation.

> **PROBLEM 9** Construct a stock for testing the phenotype of four doses of $P[w^+,\,odd^+]$ on an $odd$ mutant background, starting with P inserts on the $X$ and third chromosomes. (*Note:* a $P[w^+,\,odd^+]$ insert on the $X$ creates some problems for using $w$ to score the presence of the P-element.)

## Pitfalls

*How Many Flies?*

The viability problems that come from using multiple dominants and balancers have been alluded to already. In general, the more that are piled into the same fly, the sicker the fly. The sicker the fly, the more you need to start with at the beginning of the scheme. Otherwise, you may find yourself at the end of a 3-month, multigenerational scheme, only to be left with one male of the correct genotype who turns out to be sterile.

You can get a rough idea of how hard it will be to obtain the flies you need by figuring out how few of the progeny from each cross are the ones you want. Usually, they are theoretically 1/8 or 1/16. Poor viability of markers and nonhomologous segregation of multiple balancers reduce the number further. Unlike cloning, the products cannot be amplified at each step, so you must start with enough to get you through—as in organic synthesis.

A simple rule of thumb is to aim for enough flies to do at least one full bottle cross for the last generation of a scheme. Given the viability problems discussed, a bottle cross will require roughly 40–50 virgins. Working backward, this suggests that the initial crosses in a scheme for manipulating two chromosomes should be started with several bottles each and will thus require 100–150 virgins.

### Which Sex?

The choice of which sex to use at each step of a scheme is influenced by several factors. One already mentioned is the lack of exchange in males. This makes it possible to use a dominantly marked chromosome as if it were a balancer, a technique used many times in the examples in this book (e.g., *Sco/odd*). A second factor is the trouble associated with multiple balancers in females, to which males are oblivious (so what else is new?).

A third factor in choosing the sex at each step is the problem of non-virginity. Despite our best efforts, non-virgins do sometimes sneak through our fine net. The presence of a few non-virgins in a cross can totally subvert the scheme, since a given set of markers can apply to more than one genotype. By taking a careful look at each cross, it will be clear that in some cases non-virginity will not be a problem because the desired progeny will be uniquely marked whether or not all of the mothers are virgin.

This is not an argument against collecting virgins for your crosses; there is still the matter of how tiny a fraction of the progeny are the ones you want. It is simply another consideration for making the schemes work in the end. Take an example from an earlier cross (p. 68):

$$\male\male \ \frac{In(2LR)O,Cy}{+} \ ; \ \frac{TM3, Ser}{ftz} \quad \times \quad \frac{Sco}{eve} \ ; \ \frac{TM6, Ubx}{+} \ \female\female$$

$$\downarrow$$

$$\frac{In(2LR)O,Cy}{eve} \ ; \ \frac{TM6, Ubx}{ftz}$$

To determine whether you are at risk, consider the markers you are seeking in the desired progeny (*Cy* and *Ubx*) and see if it is possible to get the same combination of markers from a non-virgin. In order to determine this, you must consider the cross that produced the virgins and what rogue males might have been present in the bottle with them. Could the $In(2LR)O,Cy/+$; TM3, Ser/ftz virgins have mated with males carrying TM6, Ubx such that you could potentially get Cy with Ubx in the progeny of a non-virgin? In this case, the earlier cross was:

$$\text{♀♀} \quad \frac{TM6,\ Ubx}{ftz} \quad \times \quad \frac{In(2LR)O,Cy}{Sco}\ ;\ \frac{TM3,\ Ser}{Sb} \quad \text{♂♂}$$

$$\downarrow$$

$$\text{♀♀} \quad \frac{In(2LR)O,Cy}{+}\ ;\ \frac{TM3,\ Ser}{ftz}$$

so it is clear that the virgins could have mated with TM6, Ubx males and thus produce misleading progeny with the appropriate markers but the wrong genotype on other chromosomes. Hence, you are at risk and should be scrupulous about ensuring virginity.

## MANIPULATING THREE CHROMOSOMES

Just as in juggling, where there is a major gap in going from three balls to four, so in chromosome manipulation the great divide is between two chromosomes and three. Fortunately, three chromosomes are rarely needed. Even rarer, in fact nearly unheard of, is the need to maneuver all four chromosomes at once. The principles are the same as in two-chromosome schemes, but the problems are magnified. It gets harder to make genotypes that are uniquely distinguishable, and the likelihood of ending up with one sterile male (at most) is greater. If you are not likely to need such esoteric techniques, or are uninterested in such matters, you may want to skip to the next section.

In the past, such elaborate schemes were mainly needed for certain kinds of mosaic experiments—the generation of individuals with a mixture of mutant and wild-type cells (see Chapter 6). The stocks thus generated were used to produce gynandromorphs (X-chromosome mosaics) under the influence of an autosomal mutation that induces chromosome loss. In addition, such stocks make use of a duplication on the X to cover the mutation being studied, which is recessive and lies on an autosome. Thus, when X-chromosome mosaicism is induced, the individual is also mosaic for the autosomal locus duplicated on the X. Kankel and Hall (1976) used this kind of system in their fate map study of the nervous system with an enzyme marker, acid phosphatase ($Acph$). The challenging stock they had to make consisted of:

$$\frac{X\text{-}Acph^+}{\widehat{XX}y^2} \quad \frac{pal; Acph^n}{pal; Acph^n}$$

The designation $X\text{-}Acph^+/\widehat{XX}y^2/Y$ indicates that males in the stock have the $X\text{-}Acph^+/Y$ and females have $\widehat{XX}y^2/Y$. $Acph^n$ is the mutation being made mosaic. It is a mutation in the enzyme alkaline phosphatase ($n$ is for null, actually allele number $n11$) and it served as a histochemical marker for lineage analysis during development. $X\text{-}Acph^+$ is an $X$ chromosome with a duplication of the $Acph$ locus on it, and $pal$ is the mosaic-producing mutation paternal loss. To produce mosaics, males of this stock were mated to $y$; $Acph^n$ females (for details, see Chapter 6). For the sake of posterity, Jeff Hall's mating scheme used to generate it is included here. It is long and almost as difficult to understand as to carry out. Consider it a challenge and a test of your growing fly genetic acumen. If you are still baffled after studying it, don't despair—schemes of this complexity are like a path to Zen.

♂
$$\frac{Cy}{Pm} ; \frac{TM6}{Sb}$$
×*
♀
$$\frac{\widehat{XX}y^2}{Y}$$
×
♂
$$\frac{y}{y^+Y} ; \frac{pal}{pal}$$
*Same cross, so instead of discarding the parents, transfer them to fresh bottles

↓ ↓

✝ ♀
$$\frac{\widehat{XX}y^2}{Y} ; \frac{Cy}{+} ; \frac{TM6}{+}$$
×
♂
$$\frac{y}{y^+Y} ; \frac{Pm}{pal} ; \frac{TM6}{+}$$

♀
$$\frac{\widehat{XX}y^2}{Y}$$
×*
♂
$$\frac{Cy}{Pm} ; \frac{TM6}{Sb}$$

↙ ↘ ↙

♀
$$\frac{\widehat{XX}y^2}{y^+Y} ; \frac{Cy}{pal} ; \frac{+}{+}$$
×
♂
$$\frac{+}{Y} ; \frac{Cy}{pal} ; \frac{TM6}{+}$$

♀
$$\frac{\widehat{XX}y^2}{Y} ; \frac{Cy}{+} ; \frac{Sb}{+}$$
×
♂
$$\frac{X\text{-}Acph^+}{Y} ; \frac{Acph^n}{Acph^n}$$

↓ ↙

♀
$$\frac{\widehat{XX}y^2}{Y} ; \frac{pal}{pal} ; \frac{TM6}{+}$$
×
♂
$$\frac{X\text{-}Acph^+}{Y} ; \frac{Cy}{+} ; \frac{Sb}{Acph^n}$$

↙ ↘ ↘

✝ ♀
$$\frac{\widehat{XX}y^2}{Y} ; \frac{Cy}{pal} ; \frac{TM6}{Acph^n}$$
×
♂
$$\frac{X\text{-}Acph^+}{Y} ; \frac{Cy}{pal} ; \frac{TM6}{Acph^n}$$

✝ Unhealthy females; use lots of them.

## MAKING REARRANGEMENTS

There have been a few virtuoso practitioners of chromosome rearranging in the history of *Drosophila* genetics. H.J. Muller was the first (in this, as in so many other things), Ed Novitski the grand master, and Loring Craymer the most recent (for details and references, see Ashburner 1989). Deletions, duplications, and translocations are the classes of rearrangements that you are likely to make, and of these, deletions are the most commonly needed. In general, rearrangements can be made from scratch, i.e., from normal chromosomes, or from preexisting rearrangements. Usually the process requires some kind of agent, such as radiation or chemical mutagens. In some cases, they can be made by exchange events between rearrangements. Above all, it is important to consult the Red Book (Lindsley and Zimm 1992), FlyBase, and the stock collections to make sure the chromosome you want does not exist already.

The universal rule for making rearrangements is that it is always easier to start from some preexisting rearrangement.

### Inducing Deletions

The best way to induce deletions is to call (or e-mail) the Bloomington Stock Center and request that they be sent to you. When this is not possible, producing a deletion by radiation or chemical mutagenesis is very much like inducing a new recessive allele of a gene (see Chapter 2): You carry out a complementation test of the treated chromosomes. If you start with a wild-type chromosome and want to delete a region containing an easily scored, visible marker, simply treat normal males with the agent (radiation or chemicals), mate to females homozygous for the marker, and recover progeny displaying the marker phentoype.

The scheme outlined below takes a shortcut that was eschewed in Chapter 2, namely screening in the F1 generation. The rationale for doing it here is that deletions generally span more than one locus, do not arise with great frequency, and are almost always homozygous lethal. Thus, you can afford to take the trouble of separating out the chromosomes in the F2 generation because it allows you to throw out so many of the F1s. It may be necessary to screen 10,000 or more mutagenized chromosomes. The limitation is that this approach only works with visible markers, but since deletions are hard to get, it's worthwhile trying to find a way to do it with visible markers.

Mutagenized    $\dfrac{+}{+}$ × $\dfrac{en^1}{en^1}$    $en^1$ is a viable allele of the engrailed locus,
males    a locus that can mutate to lethality

$\dfrac{en^1}{-(\ )-}$    Any progeny that look engrailed will have a newly induced allele or deletion – symbolized $-(\ )-$. If it is a deletion, it is likely to be homozygous lethal, which is testable by separating the two chromosomes and testing each for homozygous lethality and then retesting for failure to complement engrailed. For many loci, including *en*, new alleles are likely to be lethal themselves and can be handled the same way.

$\dfrac{en^1}{-(\ )-}$ × $\dfrac{In(2LR)O,Cy}{Sco}$

$\dfrac{In(2LR)O,Cy}{-(\ )-}$ or $\dfrac{In(2LR)O,Cy}{en^1}$ or $\dfrac{Sco}{-(\ )-}$ or $\dfrac{Sco}{en^1}$ × $\dfrac{In(2LR)O,Cy}{Sco}$

Mate males individually to *In(2LR)O,Cy/Sco*, collect *Cy*, non-*Sco* progeny, and mate sibs together. Vials producing no $Cy^+$ progeny are possible deletions. Confirm first by seeing that they uncover *en* and ultimately by cytology to determine breakpoints.

$\dfrac{In(2LR)O,Cy}{-(\ )-}$ × $\dfrac{In(2LR)O,Cy}{-(\ )-}$

A dominant allele at or near the locus you want to delete works just as well. Here you screen for reversion of the dominant phenotype. This can also be done as an F1 screen. (Warning!! Not all dominant mutations are revertable. Dominants that are due to haplo-insufficiency [e.g., *Ubx* or the class of mutants known as Minutes] are not. Those that are revertible represent gain-of-function mutations, hypermorphs, neomorphs, or anti-morphs, discussed further in Chapter 5.) Note that all $P[w^+]$ inserts are dominant if the fly is mutant at the *w* locus. Since these inserts are just about ubiquitous, it is now possible to "revert a dominant" almost anywhere.

Of the mutagens described in Chapter 2, radiation (specifically X-rays) has been used most commonly to induce deletions and is generally preferable to chemical agents in its reliability, although the frequency of recovering such deletions is on the order of 1–5/10,000 using 4000r. Up to half of the recovered X-ray-induced alleles at a locus are multi-locus deletions (Pastink et al. 1987, 1988). Large ones are rarer than small ones. As in other kinds of mutagenesis, mature sperm are the most sensitive. EMS mutagenesis, traditionally thought to be a point mutagen, has been found over the years to produce many deletions as well. Many of these are small and intragenic, which is an ideal way to generate a null allele (see Chapter 5) without taking out other genes.

P-element excision has also been widely used for producing small deletions. Imprecise excisions produce deletions that are generally small (up to 2 kb) and thus usually intragenic, but larger deletions also occur (for references and details, see Ashburner 1989). The frequency of producing such deletions is as unpredictable as any P-element transposition event, depending in large part on the site of insertion.

Excision schemes are set up to detect loss of the wild-type allele of an eye-color marker such as $w^+$ in the P-element, following the same general principles outlined earlier for induction of new mutations by P-elements. For a lethal, $w^+$ insertion on chromosome 3, the scheme would go like this:

$$\frac{w}{Y} ; \frac{P[w^+]}{TM3, \, Ser} \quad \times \quad \frac{w}{w} ; \frac{Sb \, P[ry^+ \, \Delta \, 2-3]}{TM6, \, Ubx}$$

$$\downarrow$$

Select $Ser^+ \, Sb$ males $\quad \frac{w}{Y} ; \frac{P[w^+]}{Sb \, P[ry^+ \, \Delta \, 2-3]} \quad \times \quad \frac{w}{w} ; \frac{TM6, \, Ubx}{Sb}$

$$\downarrow$$

Select $w$, $Sb^+$, $Ubx$ males $\quad \frac{w}{Y} ; \frac{-(\;\;)-}{TM6, \, Ubx} \quad \times \quad \frac{w}{w} ; \frac{TM6, \, Ubx}{Sb}$
and mate to balancer
stock to test for lethality

The frequency of obtaining such P-element excisions depends on both the sequences in the P-element and the site of insertion. The ratio of precise to imprecise excisions, which will influence the recovery of deletions, also varies but tends to favor those that are imprecise. Of those that are imprecise, however, most are not deletions but are excisions that have left behind a piece of the P-element. Thus, the induction of new deletions may be as rare as 0.1% and as common as 10% of chromosomes screened. The frequency of imprecise excisions can be increased if the chromosome bearing the P-element is unable to pair with its homolog and use it as a template for repair (Engels et al. 1990). The virtue of the genetic screen outlined above is that it allows one to score simultaneously for excision (loss of $w^+$) and lethality.

The ability to recover a deletion will depend on what loci are being uncovered. If the region you want to delete contains a haplo-lethal locus, you are in big trouble. If it contains some other kind of haplo-insufficient locus, such as sterility, you are also in trouble. Even if it only contains a locus that is unhealthy in one dose, such as a Minute locus, you will have a hard time. (Minutes are a class of loci, encoding ribosomal proteins, sprinkled around the genome that have a similar hemizygous phenotype: thin bristles, retarded development, small size. In addition to being haplo-insufficient, they are also recessive lethal. For detailed discussion, see Ashburner [1989].)

## Synthesizing Stable Deletions from $T(Y;A)$s

In keeping with the principle that it is better to make rearrangements from preexisting ones, the $T(Y;A)$s described above (Chapter 3, Synthesis of Deletions and Duplications) are sometimes a good starting point for making deletions.

One generates flies carrying a deletion by crossing two $T(Y;A)$ stocks bearing different breakpoints (different points along the autosome and different arms of the $Y$ so that the $y^+$ and $B^s$ markers are oppositely arranged):

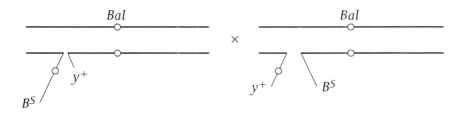

Both of these stocks look $y^+$ and $B^s$. The deletion-bearing progeny will lack $B^s$ and will have two doses of $y^+$.

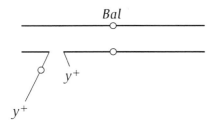

It is possible to collect males and virgin females of this $y^+$ $B^+$ genotype and set up a stock. Such a stock, however, does not thrive, because many aneuploid progeny are produced. Since one usually wants a deletion for screening new mutations, or some other use that requires large numbers of flies, the poor viability of the stock is a liability.

It is possible to reattach the autosomal pieces in this stock by irradiation to produce an intact, stable deletion. An event of this sort will occur at a much higher frequency than induction of a deletion de novo, because the arms of the $Y$ present a large target and because one is inducing an exchange event between them. Since it is necessary to have both autosomal pieces of the $T(Y;A)$ present in the cell that receives the radiation, this is done in females and at a much lower dose than used in males, 1500r, so as not to produce damage in the oocyte.

The recovery of such reattachments can sometimes be made easier by using a selection scheme based on the restoration of fertility with the reattached chromosome to an otherwise sterile genotype when it is unattached (Lyttle 1984).

Selection of the reattachment is done easily by scoring loss of $y^+$ in flies otherwise mutant for yellow on the $X$ (which is already true for the $T(Y;A)$ stocks). Thus, one simply collects females from the unhealthy, synthetic deletion stock, irradiates them, mates them, and looks for $y$ progeny. Since the stock is balanced anyway, the new chromosome comes out balanced. It can then be tested to confirm that it is truly reattached by mating to one of the parental $T(Y;A)$ stocks and seeing that no aneuploids are recovered, i.e., no separation of $y^+$ and $B^s$.

## Synthesizing Deletions from P-element Insertions

P-elements have brought a new level of rationality into the generation of deletions. Since their chromosomal position can be accurately determined, they provide identified targets for rearrangement events. Since they can be mobilized to insert at new sites easily by a simple cross (see Chapter 2 on mutagenesis), new insertions can be readily obtained. More importantly, there is a nonrandom probability that transposition will occur to a site relatively near the original site. This means that if a mechanism existed to catalyze chromosome breakage and rejoining at these P-element insertions, a technique could be developed for the rational synthesis of deletions and duplications by unequal crossing-over.

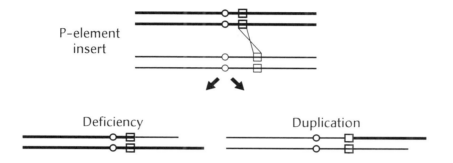

Golic (1994) devised a strategy for making P-elements into sites of interchromosomal recombination. He introduced target sites for the yeast flip recombinase target (FRT) sequence into P-elements and made transformants carrying these sequences at various sites. (Other uses of this technique for analyzing time and place of gene action are discussed in Chapters 5 and 6.) He then made use of the fact that when an inserted P-element is transposed, it has a high probability of moving to a new site in the same general vicinity of the chromosome. When two homologs have such inserts in the same vicinity and the FLP recombinase is induced, it can catalyze an unequal recombination event between the homologs. The result is a deletion and the reciprocal duplication. (Induction of the recombinase is accomplished by heat shock of the *hsp70* promoter driving the FLP gene.)

The frequency of obtaining transpositions varies with the location and composition of the starting insert. Golic obtained a transposition rate ranging from 18/97 $G_1$ males (F1 progeny of the cross between the initial P-element and the $\Delta2$-$3$ transposase) to 97/104 $G_1$ males. Of those, 86% went to nearby regions of the chromosome. When set up as heterozygotes with inserts at different but nearby sites (~30 bands apart), the frequency of obtaining deletions and duplications was 0.7%. Although not overwhelming, it is significant and has the advantage of producing rearrangements with known, nearby breakpoints.

## Inducing Duplications

Stable duplications sometimes arise when a piece of chromosome is cut out during the X-ray induction of deletions. The excised fragment is sometimes inserted into a site on another chromosome (or elsewhere on the same one) and when the chromosome with the inserted piece segregates away from the excised chromosome, a reciprocal duplication and deletion are formed. This approach, however, is not one to use when looking deliberately for a particular duplication.

Free duplications of the $X$ are the easiest to induce. These are small pieces of the $X$, retaining its centromere and the distal tip with the $y^+$ locus on it. The technique is basically to chop out a piece of the $X$ to create a freely segregating mini-chromosome that is detectable by the dominance of $y^+$ on a $y$ background (i.e., in a female with $\widehat{XX}yf$). By retaining this marker, it is easy to select for such "free duplications" since flies better tolerate large duplications of the $X$ chromosome, especially in females, than of autosomes. The basic idea is illustrated below:

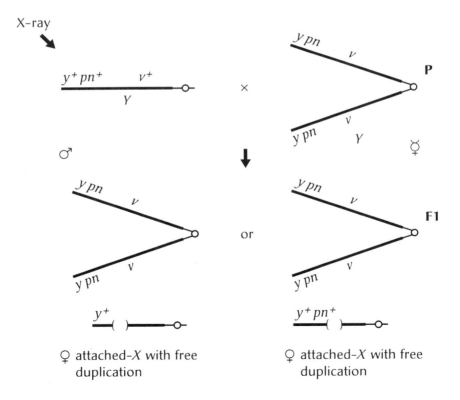

♀ attached-$X$ with free duplication

♀ attached-$X$ with free duplication

Two of many possible outcomes are illustrated here, a $y^+$ duplication and a $y^+pn^+$ duplication. These each represent possible female genotypes in progeny. The free duplications survive if they are not full-sized $X$ chromosomes. They can then be assayed for other loci they cover by mating to males with a multiply marked $X$.

Selection schemes can be designed for duplications based on their ability to rescue the phenotype of a haplo-insufficient locus. A balanced haplo-insufficient locus will appear in all non-balancer progeny unless another wild-type dose of the locus is present. Thus, irradiation of wild-type flies and mating to a balanced haplo-insufficient locus will reveal the presence of a new duplication in any non-balancer, non-haplo-insufficient progeny.

Tandem duplications—side by side on the original chromosome—can be obtained with a reasonable probability (~1/10,000) by irradiating normal chromosomes in females instead of males with a lower dose of radiation, 1500r (Ashburner 1989). This presumably results from the induction of an unequal exchange event between the two homologs, both of which are present in the irradiated oocyte.

### Synthesizing Stable Duplications from *T(Y;A)*s

For duplications, the counterpart to resealing of *T(Y;A)* pieces that works well for deletions exists in principle, but has not been tried. *T(Y;A)*s whose breakpoints are relatively near the end of a chromosome arm can be used, however, to attach an autosomal piece onto the $X$ chromosome in a fairly reliable manner.

This technique relies on detaching an attached-$X$, an exchange event between the $Y$-derived heterochromatic portion of a *T(Y;A)* and the heterochromatic regions near the centromere of an attached-$X$ chromosome, helped along by a little radiation. Heterochromatic regions have rough homology with each other and will recombine with a low probability (1/1000) that can be boosted by radiation.

Most attached-$X$s are not suitable for this maneuver, since they are generally deleted or rearranged for most or all of their centric (centromere-linked) heterochromatin. There is good reason for this: Since attached-$X$ stocks are usually kept with a free $Y$ chromosome, they would detach spontaneously if heterochromatic pairing and exchange could occur. The particular attached-$X$s that are suitable for this technique retain their centric heterochromatin and are thus not good for normal stock maintenance, e.g., *C(1)RM, y pn v*. One simply crosses the *T(Y;A)* into that attached-$X$ stock, irradiates females, and mates them to unmarked males.

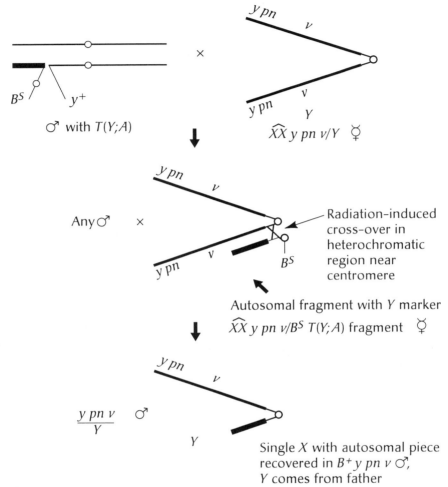

The resulting product is an $X$ chromosome linked to the terminal fragment of an autosome. It is recognizable because males will not receive the recessive markers on the attached-$X$ unless there has been a breakdown. Thus, one looks for a male with $y$ $pn$ $v$ but not $B^s$ (or $y^+$, depending on the $Y$ breakpoint). The size of duplication that will be viable depends on which autosomal arm it comes from (see above).

## Synthesizing Attached-$X$s

A new attached-$X$ can be made in the same way just described for taking one apart. Why would you ever want to do that? If you wanted to make an attached-$X$ with, for instance, a temperature-sensitive lethal mutation on it so that the stock could be made to produce only males. The strategy is to start with an $X$ chromosome with the desired mutation on it and then allow it to recombine with an $X$ joined to a $Y$ marked with $B^s$ (called $XYS \cdot YLB^s$ and carrying $y^2\ su(w^a)$ and $w^a$);

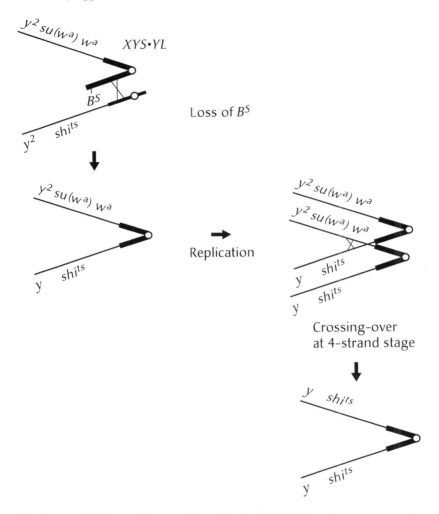

The loss of $B^s$ is easily monitored in individual female progeny who are then used to start separate strains. An attached-$X$ with arms heterozygous for different alleles is inherently short-lived, since crossing-over takes place after replication and will occur freely making various homozygous combinations of the differing markers. Here, one would again start strains from individual female progeny and test them for presence of the temperature-sensitive paralytic mutation shibire-temperature-sensitive *(shi^{ts})*.

## Autosynaptic Chromosomes and the Joys of Gibberish

One of the more esoteric backwaters of fly genetics is the synthesis of duplications and deletions from that class of inversions spanning the centromere, known as pericentric inversions:

$$a \quad b \quad d \quad c \quad e \quad f$$

The meiotic behavior of inversion chromosomes has held a strange fascination for chromosome mechanics aficionados ever since the classic and voluminous study of crossing-over in inversion heterozygotes by Sturtevant and Beadle (1936).

Pericentric inversions are relevant to the construction of aneuploids because exchange in a heterozygote produces reciprocally duplicated and deleted products:

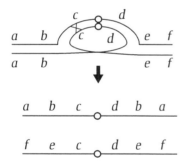

If one has access to more than one pericentric inversion of this sort, where breakpoints of one are somewhat displaced from those of the other, it is possible to generate tandem duplications and deletions of the region of chromosome that is displaced between the two.

$$a \quad b \quad e \quad d \quad c \quad f \qquad a \quad d \quad c \quad b \quad e \quad f$$

$$a \quad b \quad b \quad c \quad d \quad e \quad f \qquad a \quad c \quad d \quad e \quad f$$

This occurs by a series of exchange events, the details of which are spelled out in Craymer (1981, 1984) and Ashburner (1989). The technique has the virtue of being rational and deliberate. It is limited by the availability of appropriate pericentric inversions. They too can be synthesized (see the same references), but not with great ease.

# CHAPTER 5
# Analysis of Mutations: I. Characteristics of the Allele

One of the main reasons for doing fly genetics is, after all, the analysis of mutants. There are two main kinds of genetic tests that are carried out: The first tests the phenotypic nature of the mutant defect, and the second tests the cellular site of action of the gene. The first is dealt with in this chapter, the second in Chapter 6. An obvious prerequisite to the analysis of alleles is that you must have one or more of them. In fact, as you'll see, the more the better.

## FORMAL CLASSIFICATION OF MUTATIONS

The history of mutational analysis begins, as do so many aspects of fly genetics, with H.J. Muller. Decades before anyone had a clue as to the physical basis of the gene, Muller realized that much could be inferred about the nature of gene action from comparing the phenotypes and interactions of different alleles. In the late 1920s and early 1930s, when he was developing these ideas, the goal was primarily to understand what a gene actually was. In the 1950s and 1960s, this approach became a mainstay of microbial genetics and played a particularly important role in early studies of gene regulation in bacteria. Today, the same analysis turns out to be extremely powerful in analyzing how a gene acts and has been used repeatedly to unravel developmental pathways in flies and worms.

### Principles

The overall strategy is based on examining the range of phenotypes displayed by a series of alleles. Genes can mutate either to "loss of function" or "gain of function" phenotypes. Under ideal circumstances, the available alleles span the range from complete deletion of the gene (the ultimate loss of function), through varying degrees of partial function, to alleles that confer new and different phenotypes. One does not necessarily know a priori which of these are which, but there are straightforward genetic tests to characterize each type of allele.

An obvious requirement of this approach is that the phenotypes of the various classes of mutations be distinguishable either in terms of severity or qualitative effect. Comparisons are then made by means of complementation tests and by varying the dosage (number of copies) of the gene.

This kind of analysis does not magically tell everything you may want to know about the gene you are studying. There are few hard and fast rules for what the molecular correlates will be of a particular, formal class of mutations. Much depends on the actions and interactions of the protein in question. However, it can tell quite a lot about the realm in which a gene acts. For example, if the only alleles of the even-skipped gene that existed were those that completely eliminated the gene's function (a "gene-knockout," as the mouse people are wont to say), it would never have been called "even-skipped." Read on.

### Null Alleles (Amorphs)

A mutation that completely eliminates a gene's function is a "null" allele or, in Muller's original parlance, an "amorph." In molecular terms, this can be caused by any lesion that completely blocks transcription or translation of the gene, as well as many nonsense and missense mutations. Null alleles are generally the most likely kind of mutation to be isolated, presumably due to the fact that there are many more ways to wreck a protein's ability to function or block its expression than there are to make subtle alterations in it. In organisms where it is easy to isolate multiple alleles, such as the nematode, the phenotypic class of mutants that is recovered most frequently is tentatively designated as the null phenotype. (This assumes that the mutant screen is not biased in favor of a particular kind of allele, such as demanding viable alleles of a gene that is lethal when null.)

A deletion of the locus is, of course, the quintessential null allele. Deletions are characterized on the basis of cytologically determined breakpoints in the chromosome, and thus they become the basis for an objective genetic test against which any allele can be compared. This provides a solid standard for all subsequent characterizations and does not start out depending on any particular phenotype.

The formal definition of a null allele is that it behaves no differently from a deletion of the locus in complementation tests. "Behavior" in this context refers to the phenotypes produced when combined with other alleles. A homozygous null allele should give the same phenotype as the null allele over a deletion (i.e., hemizygous):

$$\frac{null\ allele}{null\ allele} = \frac{null\ allele}{Df} = \frac{Df}{Df}$$

and these should be no different from the deletion homozygote, provided the deletion does not also uncover a lethal or another gene with an obvious mutant phenotype. ("Uncover" in this context is fly jargon for failing to complement.) Homozygous deletions are usually lethal and so this particular comparison usually requires that the mutation itself is lethal. What they all have in common is the lack of any functional gene.

There are other ways to be misled in this kind of analysis. You would mistakenly conclude that your mutant is not null if you obtained a more severe phenotype with the deficiency because there is a second mutation present on the *null*-bearing chromosome that interacts dominantly with the deficiency. Stranger things have occurred. Alternatively, if the phenotype of a null allele is indistinguishable from the phenotype of an allele with 10% of normal activity ("hypomorphic"; see below), there is no way to tell the difference.

It is not always true, however, that a missense mutation that results in an inactive protein will be equivalent to a deletion of the locus. If the protein is a subunit in a multimer, the presence of dead subunits can sometimes "poison" the multimeric complex—a situation that would not occur with a deletion of the gene. This serves only to underline the fact that the formal characteristics of a mutation depend on the actions and interactions of the protein in question.

## Hypomorphs

Mutations that produce a partial loss of function are called "hypomorphs." At the molecular level, these usually consist of lesions that reduce the level or efficiency of the gene product. This can occur at the level of transcription; transposable element insertions frequently reduce transcription as a consequence of their disruption of 5′untranslated regions (Ashburner 1989). Similarly, a reduction can occur at the level of protein function as a consequence of missense or nonsense mutations that reduce protein activity or increase turnover.

Hypomorphs produce a graded series of phenotypes with increasing copy number. That is, the homozygous state is somewhat less severe than the hemizygous state (hypomorph over deletion), and the hemizygote is somewhat less severe than the homozygous null allele (or deletion). The order of phenotypic severity is thus:

$$\frac{hypomorph}{hypomorph} \quad > \quad \frac{hypomorph}{Df} \quad > \quad \frac{Df}{Df}$$

or

$$\frac{hypomorph}{hypomorph} \quad > \quad \frac{hypomorph}{null} \quad > \quad \frac{null}{null}$$

These correspond to two, one, and zero doses of the allele, respectively. In some instances, it is possible to construct a duplication containing the mutant allele (see Chapter 4) and so construct flies with three and four doses of the hypomorph to demonstrate the increased rescue of the phenotype with additional doses. This can be done most readily with P-elements carrying the mutant gene.

In most instances, hypomorphic mutations produce phenotypes that differ only in degree from the null. The simplest and earliest examples were eye-color mutations. A more interesting contemporary example is the Toll maternal-effect locus, in which the null allele results in a fully dorsalized embryo and various hypomorphs produce a graded series of partially dorsalized embryos. Sometimes, however, as in the case of even-skipped, a hypomorphic phenotype is qualitatively distinct from the null phenotype. Null alleles of eve produce an unsegmented lawn of denticles, whereas the phenotype of missing even-numbered segments, originally so esthetically pleasing, is a hypomorphic phenotype. Thus, even qualitatively distinct hypomorphs can still represent a graded expression of the gene, especially if there is a threshold for the transition from one phenotype to another.

Temperature-sensitive mutations are usually hypomorphs. A heat-sensitive allele of the no-receptor-potential-A (norpA) locus is a case in point. At restrictive temperature, the $norpA^{H52}$ mutant produces no electrical activity in the eye (Pak et al. 1980). At permissive temperature, there is detectable electrical activity but, as revealed by intracellular recording, the normally synchronous electrical potentials are splayed out over a longer time course. This illustrates that the gene product is involved in an intermediate step of phototransduction, as opposed to the initial light absorption or final channel opening. Partial-function alleles can thus be more informative than null alleles in some instances, but it is always necessary to know the null phenotype as a baseline. Temperature-sensitive alleles always are rare, and thus it is necessary to isolate a series of alleles.

A temperature-sensitive hypomorphic phenotype does not always mean altered protein structure due to missense mutation. Depending on the protein's normal heat stability and its stoichiometric requirements, a reduced level of transcription can produce a temperature-sensitive phenotype. The sodium channel gene *para* (paralytic) illustrates this principle. The original heat-sensitive allele turned out to be a transcriptional hypomorph which nonetheless produced conditional failure of electrical conduction (Kernan et al. 1991). In the same manner, an insertional mutation can be temperature sensitive, as in the case of the original bithorax allele, $bx^{34e}$ (isolated by Calvin Bridges in *34e*, the fifth month, May, as symbolized by the fifth letter, e, of 1934). Temperature-sensitive nulls also exist (e.g., *csp*, Zinsmaier et al. 1994). These are more properly referred to as temperature-sensitive phenotypes rather than temperature-sensitive alleles.

Germ-line transformants often produce hypomorphic phenotypes due to the difficulty of achieving fully normal expression for many cloned and reintroduced genes. The hypomorphy is generally due to the lack of particular *cis*-acting controlling elements, resulting in reduced transcriptional efficiency or missing domains of expression. The lack of such flanking sequences can also make the insert more sensitive to "position effects"—influences of surrounding sequences and controlling elements on its expression. Many transformants for the period locus, governing biological rhythms, produce a "long-day" phenotype with a free-running circadian rhythm of up to 27 hours instead of 24 (Hamblen et al. 1986). These resemble heterozygous deletions of the locus as well as the $per^{long}$ alleles isolated in standard mutant screens and shown by tests over a deletion to be hypomorphs.

## Hypermorphs

Mutations that produce an excess of the normal gene product or a hyperactive version of the protein represent one kind of "gain of function" and are called "hypermorphs." The molecular phenotype of such mutations is the converse of hypomorphy. Transcription may be increased, or a missense mutation may increase the efficiency of a protein's function.

The diagnostic test for a hypermorph is that it can be corrected, or at least ameliorated, by being placed heterozygous with a deletion or with a null allele. The order of phenotypic severity would thus be:

$$\frac{hypermorph}{hypermorph} \quad > \quad \frac{hypermorph}{+} \quad > \quad \frac{hypermorph}{Df}$$

Where the hypermorphy is not extreme, the phenotype is sometimes approximated by duplications of the wild-type locus. The Confluens "allele" of the Notch locus falls into this category. *Co* is similar to a $N^+$ duplication, producing thickened wing veins, and *Co/Df* is approximately wild-type. *Co* actually turned out to be a tandem duplication of the Notch locus, correctable by unequal crossing-over to restore euploidy.

## Neomorphs

Mutations that produce a novel function are called "neomorphs." There is not much consistency in the kinds of molecular lesions that produce this second kind of gain of function. They are most easily defined in contrast to hypermorphs by the fact that they are not ameliorated when placed hemizygous with a deletion. Nor can they be fully rescued by addition of extra doses of the wild-type allele. They are distinguished by their novelty.

Neomorphy can be produced by ectopic expression of a gene—such that it appears in places or at times it does not belong. Such transcriptional lesions usually result from chromosome rearrangements that juxtapose new promoters or enhancers with the gene in question. The original Antennapedia mutation was the result of a rearrangement that induced expression in the head of a transcript normally found in the thorax (Schneuwly et al. 1987). Unregulated activity at the protein level can also produce neomorphy. This is the case for many human oncogenes and for mutations such as the constitutively active MAP kinase of the Sevenmaker mutation, which produces multiple R7 photoreceptors (Brunner et al. 1994).

Complementation tests for neomorphic mutations are problematic. Since they are not ameliorated (or worsened) when combined with a deletion, it is often impossible to see any effect when the homologous chromosome carries another mutant allele of the gene. They are, however, usually dominant for some phenotype. Thus, a good strategy for obtaining null alleles is to revert the dominant phenotype. The result is almost always a null allele (especially when done with radiation) and thus easier to map by testing for complementation with other alleles.

In cases where the null phenotype of the locus is not already known, reversion of a neomorph can be extremely informative, as shown with the aforementioined Antennapedia mutation. When subjected to chemical (EMS) mutagenesis, revertants of the dominant Antennapedia allele produced recessive lethal alleles that showed a reciprocal phenotype: transformation of leg tissue into antenna (Struhl 1981). (Since the new alleles were lethal, their effect on leg phenotype had to be studied in mosaics. See Chapter 6.)

An informative exception to the rule of obtaining nulls from reverting dominants is the case of Sex-lethal (Sxl), a gene that occupies a key place in the sex-determination hierarchy. The original allele $Sxl^{f\#1}$, which proved to be a null, is lethal when homozygous in females, whereas a dominant allele $Sxl^{M\#1}$, which proved to be constitutively active, is lethal to males (Cline 1978). Reversion of the dominant by chemical mutagenesis yielded several new alleles whose properties were crucial for making sense of Sxl. These alleles, recessive but not null, dissociated the initiating function that Sxl plays in setting off the female pathway of development from its autoregulatory function in maintaining that determined state in cells (Cline 1984).

> **PROBLEM 10**   Design the genetic crosses to recover revertants of the neomorphic Contrabithorax, a third-chromosome, dominant, viable variant of the Bithorax Complex. Be sure that you can reliably recover reverted chromosomes even if they have become recessive lethal or confer no obvious phenotype at all.

## Antimorphs

An "antimorph" is a mutation that actually antagonizes the wild-type allele and is distinguished from a neomorph by the fact that it can be rescued, at least in part, by additional doses of the wild-type gene. "Poison" subunits, mentioned earlier as an exception to the equivalence between null alleles and deletions, fall into this category.

Some of the Abruptex (Ax) alleles of the Notch locus are antimorphs in which homozygotes are viable and heterozygous combinations of alleles are lethal. Ax produces shortened wing veins, short and thin wings, and clumped bristles. For some alleles, the defect is corrected in Ax/Df but is not exactly approximated by extra doses of $N^+$. This makes sense in the context that the Notch protein is thought to act as a cell-surface receptor for signal transduction and the Ax mutations behave as if constitutively activated (Kelley et al. 1987). Extra wild-type proteins would not be expected to act this way.

## Gain Versus Loss of Function

Not all genes are capable of mutating to all possible "morphs." Some will never produce obvious gain-of-function phenotypes and others will never produce obvious loss-of-function phenotypes. It all depends on the mode and site of action of the gene's product.

Genes that are present in multiple copies (i.e., more than one per haploid genome) may be detectable only as gain-of-function mutants. This may be the only way to stand out from the crowd. Such hyper- or neomorphs, when reverted, may result in the infamous "no phenotype" phenotype (cf. Hall 1994), since they are well buffered by their cognate comrades.

Conversely, of the many extant eye-color genes of the fly, most of which are enzymes of pigment synthesis and deposition, few have ever been mutated to gain-of-function phenotypes.

Gain-of-function alleles often show phenotypes that are reciprocal in some fashion to those of loss-of-function alleles. When they do, it often means that the gene product plays a regulatory role. The molecular nature of these gene products can range from receptor-like proteins such as torso (Klingler et al. 1988; Sprenger et al. 1989) or Notch (Palka 1990; Lyman and Young 1993) to transcription factor-like proteins such as Antennapedia (Struhl 1981; Levine et al. 1983) or splicing factor-like proteins such as Sexlethal (Cline 1984; Bell et al. 1991).

## Intragenic Interactions

Back in the Cambrian period of pre-molecular genetics, much attention was paid to anomalous patterns of complementation as perhaps important clues to the nature of the gene. These "complex loci" were so-called because of a characteristic complementation between some allelic combinations but not others: e.g., $m^1/m^2$ and $m^2/m^3$ failed to complement, but $m^1/m^3$ did complement. Three of these loci, the bithorax region (Lewis 1963; and now known to be the $Ubx$ transcription unit), Notch (Welhsons 1965), and rudimentary (Carlson 1971), were studied in great genetic detail, including fine-structure, recombinational mapping of alleles within the gene. These studies succeeded in grouping some of the mutant phenotypes into particular regions of the gene, in some cases showing that alleles that complemented each other were nonetheless separable by recombination. This apparent paradox, inexplicable at a time when genes were thought of as a unit of structure as well as of function, was termed pseudo-allelism but offered no compelling explanation to the phenomenon. The cloning of these loci and identification of their gene products revealed that each one was a single, large transcription unit—although it also turned out that the Bithorax Complex was authentically complex and consisted of two more, adjacent transcription units (Lewis 1985). The complex complementation patterns resulted from separable functions within the unit or even within the protein.

"Negative complementation" was another anomaly much puzzled over in the pre-cloning days of genetic analysis. These were instances in which a heteroallelic combination of mutations produced a more severe phenotype than either homozygote: e.g., $m^1/m^2$ was worse then either $m^1/m^1$ or $m^2/m^2$. Behavior of this sort was observed for the Abruptex alleles of the Notch locus (see above and Welshons, 1965) and has been interpreted as resulting from the interaction of subunits.

## INTERACTING LOCI

So far, all our examples of gene analysis have pertained to interactions between different alleles of the same locus. Some of the most interesting doors that genetic analysis can open are those pertaining to the interaction between loci, assayed in double mutants. The construction and testing of double mutants is a tried and true technique from the early days of microbial genetics for determining whether there is an interaction between two genes or gene products. In its simplest form, one constructs a strain producing individuals mutant at two loci (see Manipulating Two Chromosomes in Chapter 4) and compares the phenotypes of each mutant separately with that of the double mutant. The nature of the interactions detected in this way can be varied—from direct physical contact between protein products to indirect contributions to a common endpoint. For this reason, such interactions must be interpreted carefully. Allele specificity (i.e., where the interaction is only apparent between certain alleles) is one way of verifying the directness of an interaction.

### Ordering Genes in a Pathway

The pathway analogy is a popular metaphor nowadays for describing the actions of genes involved in development. The paradigm for this model is the classic biochemical pathway, in which a set of gene products (enzymes) carries out sequential transformations of metabolic precursors. Metabolic pathways played a pivotal role in the history of theories on the nature of the gene, leading to the elaboration of the "one gene-one enzyme" hypothesis from work on biochemical mutants in Neurospora.

With the growth in studies of signal transduction, second messengers, and their membrane and cytoplasmic components, the pathway analogy has taken on a new incarnation. Interactions between growth factors, their tyrosine kinase receptors, and their intracellular targets have been routinely described in terms of biochemical pathways, and the critical connection between these elements and development was made by means of genetics. Interactions between mutations affecting the same developmental event made it possible to order the steps defined by each mutation—first in the nematode *Caenorhabditis elegans* and later in the fly (Avery and Wasserman 1992; Goldstein and Fyrberg 1994).

The most straightforward test is for the interaction between gain- and loss-of-function mutations in different genes of the same pathway. If a step, such as a kinase, is normally active only when stimulated by another gene product, then a gain-of-function mutation in the kinase relieves it of the stimulus requirement and makes it constitutively active. Loss-of-function mutations of genes that act prior to the kinase have no effect on its constitutive activity; the kinase mutation is epistatic (from the Greek for "stand above") to the prior-acting mutation. On the other hand, loss-of-function mutations of genes that act subsequent to the kinase block the gain-of-function phenotype by preventing the constitutive signal from reaching the end of the pathway. These, in turn, are epistatic to the kinase mutation.

Examples of this kind of interactive behavior have been obtained in studies of cell-fate determination in photoreceptor R7 ( i.e., sevenless and its friends; e.g., Brunner et al. 1994) and in the establishment of the terminal patterning system in the embryo (torso and its colleagues; e.g., Ambrosio et al. 1989). In many cases, the discovery of the interacting locus comes from mutant screens for "suppressors" or "enhancers" (e.g., Simon et al. 1991). These names refer to whether a newly isolated mutation in one gene ameliorates the phenotype of a previously isolated mutant (suppressor) or whether it exacerbates the original phenotype (enhancer). In other instances, interactions are discovered simply by making double mutants between different loci affecting the same ultimate phenotype or process.

Screens for suppressors or enhancers are simple if one screens for new dominant mutations. Because of their dominance, the new mutations appear in the F1 generation. This makes their recovery and propagation easier, while waiting to map it (see Chapters 2 and 3). For example, the screen that turned up a constitutive MAP kinase in the sevenless pathway (Brunner et al. 1994) started with a strain mutant for *boss* (bride-of-sevenless, the extracellular ligand that activates the sevenless pathway; Reinke and Zipursky 1988).

Mutagenized    ♂♂    $w^{118}$, $boss^{3991}$    ×    $w^{118}$, $boss^{3991}$    ♀♀

Progeny of this cross were tested in a behavioral assay requiring intact R7 photoreceptors. The resulting mutation, Sevenmaker, turned out to be a dominant allele of the rolled locus ($rl^{Sem}$) and was subsequently found to encode a MAP kinase (Biggs et al. 1994). Since their mutant screen demanded viability from the very start, they obtained a viable allele of $rl$, a locus for which nulls are lethal (Hilliker 1976).

Recessive enhancers or suppressors are more difficult since they require homozygosing of mutagenized chromosomes in the presence of the starting mutation.

**PROBLEM 11**    Design a screen for recessive suppressors of $Sco$ (2-51.0).

## Dosage-dependent Interactions

The genetic strategy of identifying interacting loci as a way of defining additional important contributors to a biological process has broader applicability than just pathway analysis. The pathway analogy, although of unquestioned heuristic value, fails to incorporate the nonlinear nature of many gene interactions. Gene interactions, on the other hand, occur in all sorts of situations and offer a way to begin unraveling mechanisms that might otherwise be intractable.

*Trans*-regulatory genes fit this description. Transcription factors that must form complexes or that compete for DNA sites with other such factors may be sensitive to dosage (defined as changes in copy number of a wild-type locus). If dosage alteration causes no overt phenotypic change, it can often sensitize the fly to dosage changes at other loci. By definition, these other loci interact with the first (although not necessarily in a direct fashion).

Botas et al. (1982) used this approach to identify the extramacrochaetae (*emc*) locus on the basis of its interaction with genes of the achaete-scute complex (*AS-C*). Years later, the *emc* protein was found to antagonize the binding of an *AS-C* protein complex to specific DNA sites (Van Doren et al. 1991). The existence of *emc* was revealed by mutagenizing flies that carried extra wild-type doses of *AS-C* (an insertion into the second chromosome of the X-chromosome region containing the locus $Dp(1;2)$ $sc^{19}$) and screening for progeny with extra bristles. The idea was that extra doses of the normal *AS-C* genes would throw the system off balance, making it more sensitive to alterations in the quantity (dosage) of interacting gene products. The strategy worked: The new *emc* mutation was recessive for its effects on a normal genetic background and dominant on a background of extra copies of *AS-C*. The specifics of the cross were:

Mutagenized     $\dfrac{y}{Y} \cdot \dfrac{Dp(1;2)\,sc^{19}}{Dp\,(1;2)\,sc^{19}}$ × $\dfrac{y}{y} \cdot \dfrac{Dp(1;2)\,sc^{19}}{SM5} \cdot \dfrac{TM1}{TM2}$
males

One of the virtues of this scheme is that any new autosomal mutations are automatically balanced in the F1 generation, as well as revealing any dominant phenotypes in that generation.

## CONDITIONAL ALLELES

Many of our favorite analytical tools in contemporary fly genetics trace their origins to the days when the nature of the gene was the premier question. Recombination mapping, Muller's classification of "allelo-morphs," even mutagenesis itself all served the same goal. Conditional mutations share the same history. They emerged as a focus of study to prove the "one gene-one enzyme" hypothesis of the 1940s and became a mainstay of microbial genetics. In the late 1960s, David Suzuki brought the technique to *Drosophila* and launched a major campaign to isolate temperature-sensitive mutations in a variety of different kinds of genes (Suzuki et al. 1976).

Temperature sensitivity is the most common of several kinds of conditional mutation, and sensitivity to heat is more common than to cold. Such mutations are often due to amino acid substitutions, although occasionally they can be caused by insertions that make transcription conditional. (Temperature-sensitive alleles must be distinguished from mutations that reduce transcription levels of thermolabile processes. Thus, in the case referred to above for the sodium channel locus *para*, reduced numbers of sodium channels in the membrane produced a heat-induced failure of action potentials—a function of the kinetics of sodium and potassium channel opening [Stern et al. 1990].) Alternatively, the removal of a subunit from a hetero-multimer can also produce a thermolabile phenotype. In such a case, as seen with the *csp* (cysteine-string-protein) mutant, the mutation can be null and still produce a temperature-sensitive phenotype (Zinsmaier et al. 1994).

Conditional alleles are an important developmental tool because they provide temporal control over the gene's function. This is particularly important for genes that are used for multiple functions or at multiple times—characteristics that are not at all uncommon (Hall 1994). Depending on the "leakiness" of the mutation, it may be possible to turn the gene completely on or completely off by means of shifting flies from one incubator to another at any time in the life cycle. For lethal mutations, this means that the gene's action can be assayed at stages of the life cycle later than the usual lethal phase, as has been done extensively with the temperature-sensitive Notch allele $N^{ts1}$ (e.g., Cagan and Ready 1989). Even if lethality is not bypassed, a later phenotype can be revealed that would have been overshadowed by a more dramatic earlier one, as in the use of the temperature-sensitive even-skipped allele $eve^{ID19}$ to study the gene's role in neuronal wiring after its role in segmentation of the epidermis has been completed (Doe et al. 1988). For behavioral mutations, where it is important to distinguish effects on development from those on acute physiology, conditional alleles permit abrogation of the gene's product posteclosion, as with neurotransmitter mutations such as choline acetyltransferase (Greenspan 1980). Because they are so useful, it is wise to check new mutations for temperature sensitivity. Even when a mutant screen is not specifically designed to yield conditional alleles, sometimes it does, as in the case of $eve^{ID19}$ referred to above.

Temperature-sensitive alleles also permit the defining of critical periods for particular phenotypes. For genes that are expressed throughout the life cycle, such as those involved in sex determination (Belote and Baker 1982), this is not otherwise a simple matter to determine (although there are mosaic techniques that give some of the same information, discussed in Chapter 6). The strategy for defining a temperature-sensitive period (TSP) is to set up a series of timed cultures, half at permissive temperature and half at restrictive temperature. At regular intervals during the life cycle, cultures are shifted from one temperature to the other, and in the end, the percentages of individuals with mutant or wild-type phenotypes are scored. Each set generates a curve, reciprocals of each other. The point at which they move off their plateaus defines the boundaries of the TSP, and the point of intersection is taken as its midpoint (see Fig. 1).

Some genes are refractory to the induction of temperature-sensitive alleles, presumably due to the extraordinary thermostability of their protein products. When this occurs with proteins that form homo-multimers, conditional genotypes can sometimes be synthesized by appropriate combinations of alleles that are nonconditional as homozygotes. Only in this fashion could heat-sensitive genotypes be obtained at the Ace (acetylcholinesterase) locus (Greenspan et al. 1980). As a rule of thumb, if one screens for mutants at high temperature (29°C), roughly 10% of the alleles recovered at a locus will be normal or less severe at low temperature.

Cold-sensitive mutations, although rarer, have also been recovered from mutant screens. They afford the same ability to define TSPs and turn the

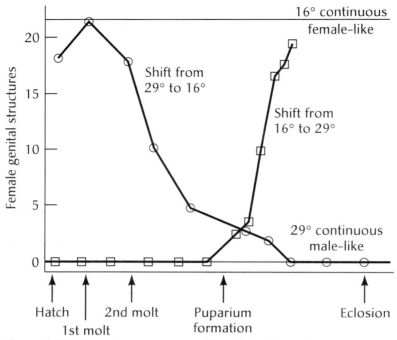

**Figure 1** TSP for a temperature-sensitive allele of transformer-2. Redrawn, with permission, from Belote and Baker (1982).

gene on and off at will. They have the advantage that heat is often more disruptive to wild-type processes than cold, particularly in some behavioral assays. They also provide interesting and unusual phenotypes, as in the cold-sensitive allele of the acetylcholinesterase gene, $Ace^{j29}$, which differed from all of the heat-sensitive genotypes by being conditionally lethal, but retaining enzyme activity even at restrictive temperature (Greenspan et al. 1980).

## Inducible Promoters

The use of transgenes driven by heat-shock promoters serves the same purpose as conditional alleles, similarly permitting temporal control over gene expresson. Heat shock has the advantage of being well defined as a phenomenon and, because a transgene is being induced, the parameters of induction, persistence, and decay can be accurately determined. It is limited, however, by the inability to give sustained expression (the induction temperature of 37ºC is too high for long exposures) and by only being able to turn on, not turn off, a gene.

Stable induction has become possible with the introduction of the FLP–FRT system derived from yeast (Golic and Lindquist 1989). This technique involves a site-specific excision by an enzyme (FLP), placed under heat-shock control, acting on its target sequences (flip recombinase targets; FRTs) to unblock the expression of a transgene (Struhl et al. 1993). The strategy is to take a 3′ transcriptional termination sequence ("Poly[A]," below), flank it with FRTs, and introduce it into a clone of the gene one wants to control. This construct is then introduced into embryos to derive germ-line transformants. These flies will not express the blocked gene until a FLP enzyme is expressed in those cells to excise the FRT-flanked blocker. To accomplish this, one need only perform a cross to combine hs-FLP with the FRT-blocked gene.

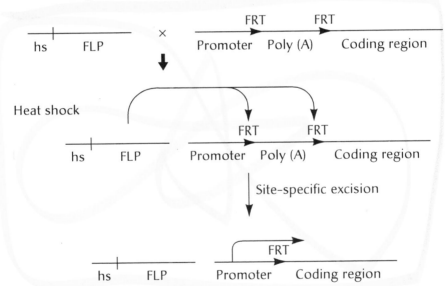

The advantage of the FLP-FRT system over plain heat shock is that once a gene is activated, it stays activated.

In the initial study, a wild-type white gene was excised (the symbol is >$w^{hs}$> for a FRT-flanked sequence) in a fly otherwise mutant at the $w$ locus (Golic and Lindquist 1989). Pupae roughly halfway through the pupal period were heat-shocked for either 60 or 80 minutes at 37°C or 38°C. When scored as adults, 100% of the individuals showed some $w$ eye tissue. The later the heat shock, the smaller the proportion of excisions in the eye. After the time that cells in the eye disc cease dividing, no more excisions could be induced, presumably as a consequence of a requirement for division to complete excision. In the non-heat-shocked siblings, 8% showed some *w* eye tissue, due presumably to low-level expression of the uninduced *hs-FLP*.

## MAINTENANCE OF MUTANT PHENOTYPES

Mutations are defined as stable changes to a gene, so it may seem silly to bring up the question of how to maintain mutant phenotypes. But it is one of the endless fascinations and frustrations of genetics that mutant stocks can lose their phenotypes over time. The problem is most acute when mutation-bearing chromosomes are kept homozygous. There is selection pressure in the culture for any other variations in the population, no matter how subtle and otherwise invisible, that will ameliorate the effects of the mutation you are trying to maintain. In the extreme, the mutant phenotype is lost all together. The fly jargon for this is "accumulation of modifiers"—a description that makes it sound like we know what is happening. (The trivial explanation for loss of a mutant phenotype is contamination of the stock. If you have kept the mutation on a chromosome that also carries an obvious recessive marker, then you can tell instantly if this is the source of the problem.)

Outcrossing is the standard remedy for retrieving a strong phenotype, since it presumably undoes the fixing of "modifiers." The simplest form of outcrossing is to mate the flies carrying the mutation to a stock with a balancer for that chromosome, pick up heterozygous males and females and then mate them to re-homozygose the mutation. This works well if the modifiers are not on the same chromosome as the mutation. If the modifiers are linked, it is necessary to allow the mutation-bearing chromosome to recombine freely with a wild-type chromosome and then re-isolate the mutation—as described in Chapter 2 for cleaning up a mutagenized chromosome.

The problem can sometimes be prevented simply by keeping stocks heterozygous (balanced). If the mutation is viable, however, this requires some effort, since you will need to select heterozygous balanced progeny each generation.

# CHAPTER 6
# Analysis of Mutations: II. Mosaics

Multicellularity begs a whole set of questions about gene action that the practitioners of phage and bacterial genetics never had to contend with: What are the consequences for mutant analysis of differential gene expression in the various cells of the organism? Where does a gene act? Which cells must be mutant to produce a mutant phenotype? Is the mutant phenotype a direct result of aberrant gene action in the affected cell(s) or the indirect result of cell interactions? Questions of this sort have become increasingly prominent as studies of development and behavior have progressed. The genetic way to address these questions is through the use of mosaic analysis.

Mosaicism occurs when the normal mitotic process of parceling out the same genetic material to each cell is subverted. The result is an individual whose cells are not all identical in genotype. If the difference between the two populations of cells is that of mutant versus normal, you have an experimental situation in which the kinds of questions listed above can be asked. In addition, mosaics also permit the tracing of cell lineages and the analysis of lethal mutations at late stages of the life cycle when lethality would already have occurred.

## Principles

Genetic mosaicism occurs in nature as part of normal life. X-inactivation in female mammals and the switching of immunoglobulin and T-cell receptor genes in lymphocytes are the best-known examples. Mosaicism that is not part of normal life also occurs in various human chromosome disorders (e.g., Down's or Turner's syndromes) where the individual is aneuploid in some tissues and not in others. These mosaics are the result of aberrant chromosome segregation during mitosis such that all cells did not receive the same chromosomes.

Mosaics can be induced experimentally by causing chromosome loss during mitosis, by inducing mitotic recombination between heterozygous homologs, or by causing excision of a DNA sequence that regulates a gene's expression. In all cases, there must be a preexisting genetic difference that is highlighted by the loss of a dominantly acting allele or synthetic transgene. Expression mosaicism can also be produced by tissue-specific control of expression of transgenes.

The ability to recognize mosaics is just as important as the ability to induce them. In particular, whether doing an experiment to determine which cells must be mutant to produce a defect or tracing a lineage, it is crucial that the genetically different populations of cells be clearly marked. It is equally crucial that the marker be as benign as possible so that the only effects on phenotype are due to the mutation under study. There are physical methods for making mosaics as well, such as tracer injection (Technau 1986) and nuclear mixing (Lawrence and Johnston 1986), which are outside the purview of this book (see Ashburner 1989; Goldstein and Fyrberg 1994).

The power of the technique derives from the fact that no two mosaics are ever alike (almost), whether induced by chromosome loss, in which the orientation of early cleavages in the fly embryo is not uniform, or by mitotic recombination, in which random cells are singly affected. As a consequence, many different juxtapositions of dividing lines between mutant and normal cells are possible.


## CHROMOSOME LOSS

Induced loss of the $X$ chromosome has been one of the most commonly used strategies for mosaic analysis in the fly, beginning (as with so many other things) with Alfred Sturtevant's studies of the claret mutation in *Drosophila simulans* (Sturtevant 1929). Since chromosome loss produces gross aneuploidy, one can only obtain viable mosaics after loss of an $X$ chromosome in females, a marked $Y$ chromosome in males, or a chromosome 4. Loss of an $X$ in a female zygote produces a gynandromorph—part male, part female—which is perfectly viable as long as the loss event occurred early enough in development (i.e., pre-blastoderm cleavage stages) to avoid lethality problems associated with lack of dosage compensation of $X$-linked genes in the islands of $XO$ cells. Loss of chromosome 4 is viable because it is so small; although haplo-4 flies exhibit a Minute phenotype that affects growth rate.

## Uses of Chromosome Loss Mosaics

Chromosome loss is the method of choice to produce mosaics with very large clones (~20–50% of the animal) and to produce clones very early (pre-blastoderm stage), prior to any zygotic gene expression.

### Fate Mapping

The initial use of the mosaic technique was to construct a fate map of the fly embryo. Sturtevant (1929) applied the same principle to map the distance between primordial cells on the blastoderm as he had to map the recombination distance between genes on the chromosome: The more mosaic dividing lines that fall between two structures, the farther apart they must be. The assumption was that mosaic dividing lines cut across the blastoderm at random (an assumption that may hold truer for mosaic dividing lines than for recombinational events on chromosomes). Two structures that never differ in their marker genotype must be derived from a common precursor cell on the blastoderm. This idea, originally developed in his studies of *Drosophila simulans*, was expanded and applied to *D. melanogaster* by García-Bellido and Merriam (1969), for the adult cuticle, and subsequently for internal adult (Kankel and Hall 1976) and larval tissues (Janning 1978).

The fate map was constructed by scoring the presence or absence of a marker for each structure ($y^+$ vs. $y$ for the adult cuticle, enzyme staining vs. no staining for internal tissues) and then triangulating the distances of all structures from each other and from the midline. The resulting formal fate map bore a striking resemblance to the histologically derived fate map originally determined by Poulson (1950) based on sections of embryos and has subsequently been confirmed by focal ablation of cells on the blastoderm with a hot needle (Bownes and Sang 1974).

On a more local level, lineage relationships have been established between cells in the same structure, such as the ommatidia of the compound eye, where it was first shown that neither the ommatidium nor even the eight photoreceptor cells were clonally derived (Ready et al. 1976). Lineage relationships are more commonly studied by means of mitotic recombination (see below).

### Focus of Gene Action

The random nature of mosaic dividing lines produced by chromosome loss, and the fact that the loss event occurs before any zygotic gene expres-

sion, make it ideal for assessing the cellular focus for developmental mutations; that is, identifying which cells need to be mutant for the abnormal
phenotype to appear. From this, one infers which cells must normally express the wild-type gene for it to carry out its developmental function.

The technique has been used to make embryonic mosaics for mutants
in the segmentation gene runt (Gergen and Wieschaus 1985, 1986) and the
cell fate-determining gene Notch, with both external and internal markers
(Hoppe and Greenspan 1986, 1990), as well as to produce adult mosaics
for mutants in genes such as sevenless (Harris et al. 1976) and bride-of-
sevenless (Reinke and Zipursky 1988). In each case, the autonomy of the
mutation—whether the gene has its primary action in the cell type that is
primarily affected in the mutant phenotype—was determined.

Gynandromorphs have played a central role in genetic studies of behavior. In general, the large size and the contiguity of the clones ensure that
significant numbers of neurons in any given area will be simultaneously affected. More specifically, the fact that they are mixtures of genotypically
male and female cells has made them well suited to the identification of
brain regions that mediate sex-specific behaviors (Hall 1977, 1979). The
analysis essentially consists of counting up the number of times each brain
structure is male or female and correlating it with how much male behavior
the fly performs. It also contains an additional formal component, derived
from Sturtevant's original fate map calculations and designed to localize
behavioral foci when you have no idea where to look or when the focus
appears to involve large or multiple portions of the nervous system
(Flanagan 1977; Arnold and Kankel 1981).

For physiological mutations that affect function in many or all neurons,
mosaics provide a way of studying the behavioral effects of localized dis-
ruptions. Since many of these mutations are also embryonic lethals,
gynandromorphs can survive to adulthood while retaining mutant brain
regions, as was done for mosaics of acetylcholinesterase mutations
(Greenspan et al. 1980).

## Methods for Inducing Chromosome Loss

A variety of mutations that affect mitotic and meiotic segregation produce
genetic mosaics. This was the starting point for Sturtevant with the claret
mutation in Drosophila simulans, a homolog of which exists also in D.
melanogaster. The effects of these mutations are not confined to a given
chromosome, and the proportion of mosaic progeny is low for all. The

other principal technique is the unstable ring-$X$ chromosome $R(1)w^{vC}$ (also known as $In(1)w^{vC}$ because it contains an inversion), a rearrangement that is efficiently lost from early mitotic divisions.

### Ring Loss

The unstable ring-$X$ has been the method of choice whenever appropriate, because a relatively large proportion of progeny are actually mosaic and because the stock construction for its use is so simple. It limits the user to mosaicism for $X$-linked genes because it is difficult, although not impossible (Gailey et al. 1987), to transpose or translocate autosomal loci onto it. The markers to be scored must also be $X$-linked.

In a female embryo heterozygous for the unstable ring-$X$ and an $X$ mutant for yellow ($y$) and white ($w$), mosaicism is clearly visible on the cuticle and in the eye. This is the result of loss of the ring-$X$ during early cleavage divisions and subsequent expansion of the haplo-$X$ clone:

$$\frac{y\ w}{Y} \quad \times \quad \frac{R(1)w^{vC}}{In(1)dl\text{-}49,\ y\ w\ lz}$$

$$\downarrow$$

$$\frac{y\ w}{R(1)w^{vC}} \Big/ \frac{y\ w}{0}$$

Mosaic notation designates the genotype of the starting embryo on the left, separated by a slash from the genotype of the mosaic tissue on the right, where $0$ indicates the lost chromosome.

The ring-$X$ is best introduced from a female, since it has poor viability in hemizygous males. If a ring-$X$ has attained good viability in a stock, which can happen over time, it usually means that it has also become more stable and thus less useful.

The chromosome $In(1)dl\text{-}49$ is routinely used to balance ring-$X$ stocks since it carries markers that reveal mosaicism ($y\ w\ lz$) but will not recombine with the ring because of its own inversion. It is important to be able to score the presence of mosaicism, because ring instability must be selected to maintain it in the stock. Presumably, this lability of phenotype is due to the unhealthiness of chromosome loss. Unlike other examples of the infamous accumulation of modifiers (see p. 102), loss of ring instability seems to be associated with the ring-$X$ chromosome itself. Thus, selection is the only remedy.

Selection of gynandromorphs to maintain the stock may seem challenging, given the intersexual nature of these flies. The rule of thumb is that if you collect all such mosaics, at least some of them will be fertile (those that have female reproductive organs and enough of a female brain to mate with males). The recovery of mosaic progeny can be at least 20% of the potential mosaic class (i.e., $R(1)w^{vC}/dl-49$) in a well-selected stock. The size of mosaic patches averages 50% of the fly, but smaller patches (due to late loss) and larger ones (due to multiple loss events) occur with reasonable frequency (Hall et al. 1976).

Harris et al. (1976) used ring loss gynandromorphs to demonstrate that the now famous sevenless (*sev*) mutation acts in retinula cell R7 to produce the mutant phenotype. That is, the *sev* phenotype—loss of R7—is cell autonomous. Since *sev* is $X$-linked, the ring carries the wild-type allele of it. By recombining the eye-pigment mutation *w* onto the same chromosome as *sev*, and taking advantage of the fact that the retinula cells contain pigment granules that are unpigmented in cells mutant for *w*, they set up a situation in which cells that lost the ring-$X$ would be simultaneously mutant for both. They showed that all R7 cells that were recovered in mosaics were pigmented, i.e., $sev^+$; there was never a $sev^-$ R7.

The same approach was later used by Reinke and Zipursky (1988) to demonstrate that the bride-of-sevenless (*boss*) mutation, which also causes loss of R7, is *non*-autonomous to R7. It acts in R8, as shown by the fact that many $boss^-$ R7 cells were recovered, but whenever an ommatidium had a $boss^-$ R8, it was also missing R7.

The ring-$X$ works at a high enough frequency to be used in embryonic studies. Mosaic frequency makes a big difference here, since it is relatively easy to recognize rare mosaic adults by the presence of small patches of *y* cuticle, but it is much more difficult (= impossible) to pick out rare embryos. Gergen and Wieschaus (1985, 1986) used the $X$-linked denticle marker shaven-baby (*svb*) to study the cell autonomy of $X$-linked segmentation mutants in the embryonic epidermis. For this study, they linked the *svb* marker to chromosomes mutant for each of the segmentation loci, runt, armadillo, fused, giant, and unpaired. Promoter fusions, such as armadillo-*lacZ* (Vincent et al. 1994) or polyubiquitin-GFP (Davis et al. 1995), can also serve as effective mosaic markers.

Sometimes the gene to be studied can serve as its own marker. Hoppe and Greenspan (1990) used antibodies to the protein product of the $X$-linked Notch (*N*) gene as a marker of neuroblasts in embryonic Notch mosaics. Histochemistry for the enzyme acetylcholinesterase was used to mark mosaics for *Ace* mutations (Greenspan et al. 1980).

The crosses to produce embryonic ring loss mosaics require somewhat different handling than those for adults. It is very helpful if some of the non-mosaic progeny classes can be easily recognized, so that one doesn't spend even more hours looking for tiny mosaic patches in already tiny embryos that don't have a prayer of being mosaic. To achieve this end, the ring-*X* should be introduced from the father and the mutation to be uncovered should be introduced from the mother. The class of potential mosaics is still 25%, but now there is also a class of hemizygous mutant progeny—those who receive the mutation from the mother and from the father's *Y*.

$$\frac{R(1)w^{vC}}{Y} \quad \times \quad \frac{svb\ runt}{FM7}$$

$$\frac{R(1)w^{vC}}{svb\ runt} \qquad \frac{R(1)w^{vC}}{FM7} \qquad \frac{svb\ runt}{Y} \qquad \frac{FM7}{Y}$$

$$\quad 1 \qquad\qquad 2 \qquad\qquad 3 \qquad\qquad 4$$

Class 1 is the potential mosaic class. All class 3 embryos will appear entirely mutant for both genes, and thus be recognizable. Counting the number of class 3 embryos gives a reliable estimate for 25% of fertilized eggs and can thus be used as the denominator to determine embryonic mosaic frequency in class 1. Moreover, class 3 embryos need not be examined in the same excruciating detail as the others for small patches of mosaicism. Granted, there can be mosaics that are almost entirely mutant due to multiple ring loss events, but these are few and irrelevant to many studies.

### Chromosome Loss Mosaics for Autosomal Genes

The *X* is nice, but most of the fly's genes are on chromosomes 2 and 3 and, unfortunately, mitotic loss of a large autosome is lethal at a very young age (Wright 1970). To get around this problem, Lewis (1963) figured out that if you can get the wild-type locus of your gene onto the *X*, you can make mosaics for that gene by losing the *X*. This works as long as the autosomal loci for that gene are also mutant in the mosaic individual.

In Lewis' case, he used a translocation of the Bithorax complex (*BX-C*) onto the *X*: *T(1;3)O5*, and crossed it onto a ring-*X* by a double cross-over event. This produced a ring-*X* with *BX-C$^+$* on it. (This was not the unstable ring-*X*, *R(1)w$^{vC}$*, but a stable ring-*X* that he induced to be lost by a technique that is so unreliable that it is not worth mentioning here.) He then performed the following cross to ask whether bithorax produced its homeotic transformations cell-autonomously:

$$\frac{R(1;3)\ O5}{Y}; \frac{bx}{bx} \quad \times \quad \frac{y}{y}; \frac{bx}{bx}$$

All of the progeny were homozygous for *bx* and, thus, all of the females were potential mosaics, heterozygous for the ring and for *y*. The outcome was that transformed cuticle was always *y* and untransformed cuticle was always *y$^+$*, indicating cell autonomy (Lewis 1963). (All right, I'll tell how he made the mosaics: He mated very old females to very young stable ring-*X* males, a technique that no one since has ever gotten to work—this author included.)

Sometimes, it is possible to transfer a wild-type autosomal locus onto the unstable ring-*X*, *In(1)w$^{vC}$*. Gailey et al. (1987) did this by taking an *X* chromosome containing a P-element insertion of the wild-type locus for dopa decarboxylase near the middle of the chromosome arm, and allowing it to recombine by double cross-over with the ring-*X*. In principle, the same thing could be done by mobilizing a P-element and screening for its insertion into the ring-*X*. The difficulty with the latter approach is that the *w$^{vC}$* allele on the ring-*X*, which causes variegation of the white gene, makes it difficult to score the presence of either a *w$^+$* or a *ry$^+$* marker to detect the presence of the insert. More generally, the difficulty with any attempt to transfer a gene onto the ring-*X*, given its poor viability, is the necessity to recover the new chromosome in a single fly and propagate a stock from it.

A more general (and workable) approach to making gynandromorphs with autosomal loci translocated or transposed onto the *X* is to use mutations that destabilize chromosomes. Three have been used successfully, two of which, paternal-loss and claret-non-disjunctional, are known to encode components of the mitotic apparatus.

Originally isolated for its meiotic phenotype, paternal-loss (*pal*) destabilizes paternally derived chromosomes (Baker 1975). It is one of the few paternal-effect mutants in the fly. Progeny of a *pal/pal* male will be mosaic for any of his chromosomes they inherited. If chromosome 2 or 3 is lost, the embryo will die. If a female zygote loses the paternally derived $X$, she will be a gynandromorph, and if chromosome $4$ is lost, the fly will survive and will have a Minute phenotype (see Chapter 4) in the haplo-$4$ tissue. Thus, the $X$ carrying a wild-type autosomal locus must be introduced from a homozygous $pal$ father.

$$\frac{X\text{-}Acph^+}{Y}; \frac{pal}{pal}; \frac{Acph^n}{Acph^n} \quad \times \quad \frac{y}{y}; \frac{Acph^n}{Acph^n}$$

$$\downarrow$$

$$\frac{X\text{-}Acph^+}{y}; \frac{pal}{+}; \frac{Acph^n}{Acph^n} \quad \Big/ \quad \frac{X\text{-}Acph^+}{0}; \frac{pal}{+}; \frac{Acph^n}{Acph^n}$$

$Acph$ is the structural gene for acid phosphatase, $Acph^n$ is a null allele of the locus, and $X\text{-}Acph^+$ is a translocation onto the $X$ of the wild-type locus. The scheme for generating these males is outlined in Chapter 4.

The frequency of chromosome loss with $pal$ is reasonable, 1–5% (Hall et al. 1976), and the stock does not need to be selected constantly. Mosaic patch size averages 30–40%. It works at a 10-fold lower rate of loss on $Y$ chromosomes or rearrangements with $Y$-derived centromeres. This matters if one has made an $X$ with an autosomal duplication by detaching an attached-$X$ with a $T(Y;A)$, as described in Chapter 4. These sometimes will acquire the $Y$ centromere as a result of the exchange event and, if so, will be less destabilized by $pal$.

Claret-non-disjunctional $(ca^{nd})$ is the D. melanogaster homolog of the D. simulans gene Sturtevant discovered. It has since been shown to comprise two separate genes, one affecting eye pigment (claret) and the other encoding a kinesin-like component of the spindle (Walker et al. 1990). In some ways the converse of $pal$, chromosomes are destabilized that are inherited from homoyzgous mothers. Thus, the $X$ carrying a wild-type autosomal locus must be introduced from a homozygous $ca^{nd}$ mother.

The D. simulans mutation was used in the early fate-mapping and lineage-tracing studies (García-Bellido and Merriam 1969). Although the proportion of progeny with mosaicism can be as high as 20% with patch sizes averaging 50%, the mutation has the serious drawback that homozygous females are so severely impaired in meiotic segregation that their fertility is very poor (Hall et al. 1976). As a consequence, few potential mosaics are produced.

## Care of Mosaic-producing Stocks

Most variants used to destabilize chromosomes are themselves unstable. Ring-$X$ stocks tend to lose their mosaic-producing ability if simply transferred generation after generation. *pal* and $ca^{nd}$ have less of a problem. To maintain the instability of ring-$X$ stocks, it is necessary to select and it is wise to maintain the chromosome $In(1)w^{vC}$ balanced over $In(1)dl$-49, $y$ $w$ $lz$ so that mosaicism for cuticle and eye pigmentation is readily visible in every generation (see p. 107). (This balancer is viable in males and homozygous sterile in females, preventing the stock from losing the ring-$X$ altogether.) One can then recognize and select gynandromorphs, choosing those with female genitalia, and set up cultures with these as the females. A superb ring-$X$ stock produces 30% gynandromorphs out of the potentially mosaic class of progeny. A ring-X stock that has been allowed to languish may have fewer than 5%. In this case, the rescue operation must be carried out in vial cultures.

In contrast, *pal* stocks have been left homozygous for decades in stock collections and still retain their mosaic-producing prowess. Given the fact that *pal* has no effect on viability, in the end one could obtain as many mosaics in the same period of time as with the ring-$X$. $ca^{nd}$ stocks, which must be balanced or they become extinct, do not seem to degrade over time either.

**PROBLEM 12**  Design a scheme to produce mosaics by $X$-chromosome loss for Hyperkinetic (1-30.1), an $X$-linked, dominant, homozygous viable, leg-shaking mutation, using $ca^{nd}$ (3-100.7) as the mosaic producer and $y$ as the marker. Start from the simplest stocks—*Hk/Hk*, *y/y*, $TM6/ca^{nd}$, and use any other balancers or markers you wish.

## MITOTIC RECOMBINATION

Loss of a wild-type or dominant allele can also be brought about by recombination between heterozygous homologs during mitosis. Recombination can occur between chromosomes in somatic cells at a very low spontaneous rate, or it can be induced by radiation or other techniques (see below). Here, in a cell heterozygous for $w$, the wild-type (dominant) allele is made homozygous in one daughter cell and the mutant allele is made homozygous in the other:

Normal
mitosis
maintains
heterozygosity

Mitotic
recombination
subverts normal
mitosis

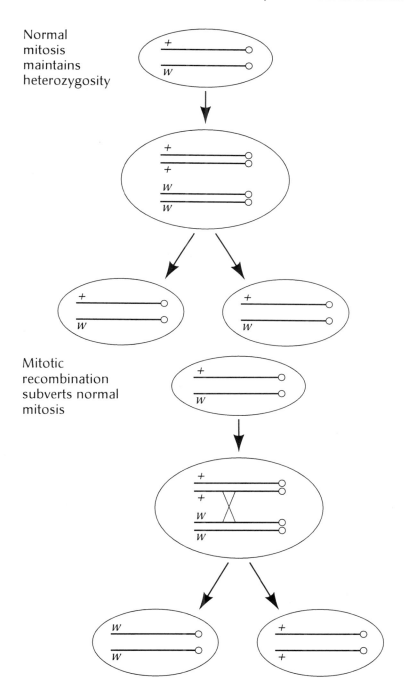

The homozygous wild-type cell will be phenotypically indistinguishable from the rest of the fly's cells, but the homozygous mutant cell will be white if present in eye tissue. The resulting daughters of the $w/w$ cell will inherit the mutant phenotype and produce a clone. Both daughter cells and their resultant clones can be marked if one includes another recessive marker in *trans*. Thus, irradiating a fly doubly heterozygous for $w$ (1-1.5) and roughest (*rst*, 1-2.2), $w/rst$ will produce "twin spots" of either nonpigmented ($w/w$) or roughened (*rst/rst*) ommatidia. Twin spots are useful for lineage-tracing studies.

The event is a random one and can thus occur in any dividing cell of the fly. Whether or not the clone will be detectable depends on whether the mutation has a phenotypic effect on that cell and its progeny. If the white mutation is made homozygous in a bristle precursor cell, you will not see it. A distinction needs to be made here between marker mutations (such as white) used for detecting mitotic recombination events and for mapping lineage, and "interesting" mutations whose effects are being assessed by means of mosaic analysis.

Marker mutations are chosen for their cell autonomy and for their gra-tuitousness; i.e., lack of effect on the developmental and behavioral pro-cesses that one uses mosaics to study. Whether you detect a patch of mosaicism by means of a marker thus depends on whether that gene is normally expressed in the cell type that has undergone mitotic recombina-tion. The marker must also lie close or proximal to the mutation it is mark-ing. (Proximal means closer to the centromere.) This ensures that there will never be a situation in which the marker is made homozygous without si-multaneously making the interesting mutation homozygous. Mitotic recombination can occur at any point along the chromosome arm, but (fortunately for this kind of analysis) tends to occur nonrandomly near the centromere.

Whether interesting mutations produce mutant phenotypes in mosaics depends on two criteria: if the mitotic recombination event has occurred in the right place and if the timing of the event is early enough to make a dif-ference. The "right place" refers to a precursor of the cells that are the focus of the mutation's effect and "early enough to make a difference" refers to the time of critical expression for the gene.

Developmental timing is crucial to the use of this technique. Some of the key findings on cell lineage restrictions in the embryo depended on careful-ly timed clone induction (Wieschaus and Gehring 1976). Consequently, the age of these progeny must be known as accurately as possible. Syn-chronized cultures are obtained by collecting freshly laid eggs over a short time span. Females that are laying eggs continually are fertilizing them just prior to laying, so time of deposition is a good measure of time of initiation of zygotic development.

## Synchronizing Age of Cultures

There is as much folklore about how to coax females to lay eggs at a brisk rate as there is about anything else in the fly world. It all boils down to the fact that if they're happy, they lay lots of eggs. The best way to make them happy is to keep them well fed in clean bottles that are not too crowded. The easiest way to do this is to place approximately 50 virgins in a fresh bottle with a large glob of yeast paste in the bottom (dried baker's yeast mixed with just enough water to thicken it to the consistency of thin peanut butter). After a couple of days, change the bottle and add males of the appropriate genotype. After another day or two, they are ready for egg collections.

Collections are best carried out for an hour at a time if irradiations and analyses will be carried out on embryos or early larvae. Longer collections are permissible for later times, since asynchronies will appear as development proceeds. The container for collection can be a little piece of desk blotter paper saturated with vinegar and yeast paste, agar plates with a thin paste of yeast, or culture bottles. The choice depends on the stage at which mitotic recombination will be induced and the stage at which the mosaics will be collected. Blotter paper is fine for embryos, agar plates for larvae, and culture bottles for pupae and adults.

The first egg collection or two is usually no good. By the third, the eggs are usually being produced full blast. (The problem with eggs collected when the females are not laying at full tilt is that the females harbor the fertilized eggs, thus confounding efforts to synchronize progeny age.) The collected eggs are then incubated for the requisite period of time, usually sometime during the larval stage, and then irradiated or heat-shocked, depending on the technique being used to induce mitotic recombination.

For careful staging of the pupal period, it is more accurate to collect white prepupae. These are recognizable as milky-looking, immobile rods, the size of third-instar larvae (which they recently were) that have taken up positions on the side of the bottle. They can be carefully picked off the side of the culture and transferred to a vial where they will complete pupation and metamorphosis.

## Uses of Mitotic Recombination Mosaics

Mitotic recombination is the method of choice for producing small clones, for controlling the time of clone induction, and for noninvasive lineage tracing. (It is also called somatic recombination, to distinguish it from the recombination that goes on in the germ cells during meiosis.)

The first use of the technique was genetic—to demonstrate that recombination could occur in somatic cells. At the same time, it was used to address an early formulation of the developmental question of which cells must be mutant to give a mutant phenotype. In Curt Stern's original formulation (1968), the question was whether one could distinguish between genes affecting "pattern" versus "pre-pattern," concepts corresponding, to some extent, with current-day notions of autonomy and non-autonomy.

### Lineage Analysis

Mitotic recombination provides the only noninvasive means of marking cell lineage. As such, it allows clones to be marked at virtually any time in development, no matter how inaccessible the tissue. The success of the technique depends on the ability to limit mitotic recombination to a single cell in the primordium being studied. Fortunately, when radiation is used to induce the recombination event, it can be calibrated so that the probability of obtaining single clones is extremely high.

Lawrence and Green (1979) introduced a clever technique for ensuring that a marked clone represents a single event, by exploiting the rarity of recombination between two mutations in the same gene. They took two different alleles of the white gene, which give a white-eyed phenotype in the double heterozygote. The rare mitotic recombination events that occurred between the two mutations would produce a normal, restored $w^+$ gene as one daughter and a doubly mutant white gene as the other. The restored $w^+$ phenotype has the virtue of appearing as a red-colored clone on an otherwise white background, making it easier to score even if small and rare.

Lineage tracing by mitotic recombination has been used most commonly on external tissues, where there are easily recognizable pigment mutations to mark the cuticle and the eye. The experiment is done by performing a cross to produce progeny that are heterozygous for a recessive marker mutation. The resulting heterozygous progeny are the appropriate targets for induction of clones. Mitotic clones have been used to establish lineage relationships in the wing (Bryant and Schneiderman 1969), the thorax

(Wieschaus and Gehring 1976), the eye (Lawrence and Green 1979), and the thoracic muscles (Lawrence 1982).

The size of a clone depends on how many divisions the affected cell has yet to go through. The relative proportion of a structure (e.g., wing) that a clone occupies depends on how many precursor cells are present at the time of clone induction. The discovery of compartments, one of the pivotal findings in fly development, arose from the use of a technique for increasing clone size by speeding up the division rate of the clone relative to its neighbors. This is accomplished through the use of Minutes, a class of mutations in ribosomal proteins that slow down development. Fortunately for the purpose at hand, they also act dominantly and autonomously (Morata and Ripoll 1975). This means that if a fly starts out as $M/+$ and has a $+/+$ clone induced during development, that cell and its progeny will outstrip its $M/+$ neighbors and occupy a greater proportion of the final structure than its progeny would have otherwise. In the course of such studies, some of the inflated clones were found to bump up against a set of boundaries in the wing disc. These boundaries divide the primordium along anterior-posterior and dorsoventral axes and were dubbed compartments (García-Bellido et al. 1973).

*Focus of Gene Action*

Any mosaic can be used to ask questions about a gene's site of action; mitotic recombination mosaics are no exception. This was Stern's original experiment in generating clones of mutant tissue for the mutation extra-sex-combs on the legs of male flies. In the original *esc* allele, male meso- and meta-thoracic legs produced ectopic sex combs as a result (we now know) of being homeotically transformed. Tokunaga and Stern (1965) induced clones in *esc/+* heterozygotes to create small patches of mutant tissue in the legs.

As in all mosaic experiments, clones must be marked to be observable. For mitotic recombination, the marker must be on the same chromosome arm as the mutation being studied so that an event that makes a mutation homozygous will also make the marker homozygous. There is leeway in one direction—it's tolerable to have the mutation homozygous without the marker, since you'll simply miss it—but not in the other—you're sunk if you make the marker homozygous but not the mutation. This is akin to scoring a false positive. The best way to ensure that you are not misled by the marker is to choose one that lies proximal to the mutation you are studying (i.e., nearer the centromere).

Tokunaga and Stern used flies heterozygous for a translocation of the wild-type locus for yellow ($y^+$) onto the tip of the left arm of the second chromosome (2L). As long as these flies were mutant for $y$ on their $X$ chromosomes, any induced recombinations of 2L would be detectable as $y$ clones. To link this marking system with the generation of *esc* clones, they needed only to generate progeny heterozygous for the *esc* mutation on the other homolog from the $y^+$ translocation. Now, whenever a mitotic recombination event makes *esc* homozygous, it will also make $y^+$ homozygous. However, as just described, this arrangement will produce $y$ clones that are not *esc* whenever the recombination occurs between the *esc* locus and the tip.

A cleaner experiment is illustrated by the use of a wing cuticle marker pawn (*pwn*) to mark clones that are mutant for the engrailed (*en*) gene, a key experiment in establishing the importance and role of compartments (Morata and Lawrence 1975). By choosing a marker that is more proximal (closer to the centromere) than *en*, they ensured that there would be no falsely marked clones (i.e., *pwn⁻* but not *en⁻*).

*Time of Gene Action*

Determination of the critical period of a gene's action was discussed earlier in the context of temperature-sensitive mutations. However, not all the genes one wants to study have temperature-sensitive alleles. In such cases, it is nonetheless possible to determine the endpoint of a gene's action by eliminating the wild-type allele at any desired stage by means of mitotic recombination. When clones are induced at successively later stages, at some point a mutant phenotype no longer results. This marks the time after which the normal gene product is no longer needed. Said timing is subject to the persistence ("perdurance" in the term coined by Antonio García-Bellido) of the normal gene product after the elimination of the wild-type allele.

Some genes, such as bithorax (Morata and García-Bellido 1976) and Sex-lethal (Cline 1984), have been shown by this technique to be required continuously throughout development. In the case of Sex-lethal, this has been explained by reason of the gene's autoregulation (Cline 1984; Bell et al. 1991).

GERM-LINE CLONES A special case of using mitotic recombination to study the time of gene action is in the distinction between maternal and zygotic effects of mutations. That is, many genes essential for oogenesis are also essential for zygotic and adult viability, making it difficult to obtain homozygous females to test for maternal effects. Wieschaus (1980) developed a clever way around this problem using dominant, female-sterile mutations. A female heterozygous for such a mutation is, by definition, sterile. If a mitotic recombination event occurs in her ovaries during oogenesis, a homozygous wild-type oocyte will sometimes arise.

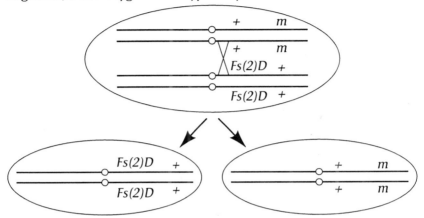

viable, fertile egg

Since it will have lost the dominant female-sterile mutation, it will complete oogenesis normally. Thus, only those eggs that have had a mitotic recombination event induced in them will successfully complete development. When another mutation is present on the chromosome arm that has become homozygous, the resulting egg will develop in the absence of that gene's product. If this gene is required for some function in the early embryo, a phenotypically abnormal embryo will result.

A clear prerequisite for this approach is that the dominant female–sterile mutation must act autonomously in the oocyte (i.e., germ line). This can be determined to a first approximation by using the same technique, since clones of somatic ovary cells likely comprise such a small proportion of the ovary that they are unlikely to rescue sterility that is somatic in origin. Confirmation can be determined independently by germ-cell transplants in which mutant germ cells are placed into a wild-type background and vice versa.

*Methods for Producing Mitotic Recombinant Clones*

RADIATION Ionizing radiation was the first method used to induce mitotic recombination, just as it was the first agent of mutagenesis. It is the simplest method, because all that is needed are an X-ray machine or radio-isotope source and some heterozygous larvae. The dose-response relationship has been well worked out. The standard rule-of-thumb dose used to maximize recombination events and minimize lethality is 1000–1500r.

The down side is that radiation is not good for cells and other living things. Some individuals are killed outright, and those that survive suffer tissue damage. The subsequent development of the tissue has thus undergone some degree of cell destruction and regeneration quite apart from the effects of any mutations made homozygous. Sometimes, the regeneration can produce pattern duplications that have nothing to do with the mutation under study.

Radiation can be delivered at almost any stage of the life cycle. The only stages that are totally sensitive occur during embryogenesis. Even so, there are windows of time during embryogenesis when radiation is tolerated well enough to yield some viable flies with mitotic clones. These are at 3 hours and after 7 hours postfertilization, reaching full survival after 10 hours (Wieschaus and Gehring 1976). Synchrony of developmental age is clearly very important for use of this technique on embryos.

THE FLP-FRT SYSTEM A kinder and gentler method for creating mitotic clones makes use of the site-specific recombinase from yeast, FLP, and its target sequence, FRT (Golic 1991). The system, introduced earlier in the context of creating deletions and of testing for the time of gene action during development, has also been adapted for the induction of mitotic recombination. The triggering event here is a heat shock to activate the recombinase. Thus, it can be induced whenever heat shock can be induced—essentially any time except pre-blastoderm embryos.

This system has the virtues of being more benign than radiation (which is not hard to be) and of ensuring that the recombination event will always occur at a predefined site on the chromosome. By knowing where the event will occur, one can assure that recombination is proximal to the markers and mutations that one wants to make homozygous. It has the double-edged feature that clones can be induced with high probability, but the likelihood of inducing single clones is correspondingly reduced.

The key to the method is the presence of FRT sites in identical positions on both homologs. It is essential that the FRT sequences on both chromosomes be oriented in the same direction, since the recombination event will only occur between identically oriented FRTs. If they are oppositely oriented, they may still recombine but will produce a dicentric chromosome and an acentric fragment (see Chapter 4).

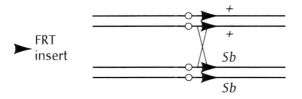

Heat shock (38°C for 60 min) was delivered at the end of the larval period and beginning of the pupal period. The frequency of individuals with mitotic clones depended on the presence of single or tandem copies of the FRT on each homolog.

| | Frequency of mosaics (%) | |
|---|---|---|
| FRT genotype | no heat shock | heat shock |
| FRT–FRT<br>FRT–FRT | 97.0 | 99.5 |
| FRT–FRT<br>FRT | 31.1 | 58.5 |
| FRT<br>FRT | 1.3 | 43.7 |
| FRT–FRT<br>+ | — | 0.3 |

Data from Golic 1991.

As this table shows, considerable spontaneous recombination occurs without heat shock when more than one FRT is present on one of the homologs. Xu and Rubin (1993) generated many strains of flies carrying double FRT insertions near the centromeres of each chromosome arm.

The FLP-FRT system also works well for the production of germ-line clones (Golic 1991). A standard treatment (1 hr at 38°C) during the mid to late pupal period produces ample progeny from females heterozygous for dominant, sterilizing mutations (see above).

## Markers for Internal Tissues

Mosaic studies of genes that do not affect the cuticle have lagged far behind those that do because of the paucity of markers and the difficulties in using them. Kankel and Hall (1976) developed acid phosphatase histochemistry as a marking system, producing a translocation of the wild-type

*Acph* locus (3-101.4) onto the *X* and then inducing loss with *pal* (see genetic scheme in Chapter 5). *Acph* works reasonably well for sections of essentially all tissues except muscle.

A good, all-purpose marking system that works at all stages and tissues from gastrulation onward has been constructed by the fusion of *lacZ* to the constitutive armadillo promoter (Vincent et al. 1994). Since it is contained in a P-element, it can be mobilized to any chromosome arm. A significant advantage of *lacZ* is that there is little background staining for its substrate X-gal (5-bromo-4-chloro-3-indolyl-β-D-galactoside) in most tissues and stages, so the insert acts as a dominant marker. The proliferation of *lacZ*-expressing enhancer-trap strains has resulted in many other potential mosaic markers on various chromosome arms. The utility of any given enhancer trap depends on whether the enzyme is expressed in the tissues one wants to use for mosaic detection.

An antigenic marker designed for use and detection in all tissues at all stages has been developed by Xu and Rubin (1993). This makes use of a domain of the *myc* protein and a commercially available monoclonal antibody specific for that epitope. The drawback of this technique is that staining for mosaicism needs to work virtually every time without a hitch, given the low frequency and uniqueness of mosaics. Antibody staining, even at its best, has difficulty meeting this standard.

## GAL4 AND EXPRESSION MOSAICISM

Promoter fusions in transgenic animals produce another kind of mosaicism based on intrinsic mechanisms of gene regulation to drive expression of introduced, cloned genes. Selective expression of the gene being studied is achieved either by fusion to a defined promoter sequence or through activation by the yeast transcription factor GAL4, itself driven as an enhancer trap.

This approach differs from clonal mosaic techniques (chromosome loss and mitotic recombination) in that the pattern of mosaicism is nonrandom, reproducible, and bilaterally symmetrical—all features of enhancer-driven transgenes. Reproducibility is a major boon to mosaic studies in which the phenotype is inconsistent, such as behavior, or the assay difficult, as in some kinds of histology.

The GAL4–enhancer trap technique offers the additional advantage of circumventing problems associated with insertion site effects on promoter fusions. Since the same GAL4–enhancer trap insert can work independently on any other transgene that has an upstream activating sequence (UAS), its pattern of expression can be assessed with a *UAS-lacZ* strain separately from its use for ectopic expression of a *UAS*-effector gene (Brand and Perrimon 1993). This technique has been used to study developmental effects of ectopic expression of even-skipped in embryos and of *Raf* expression in oogenesis (Brand and Perrimon 1993, 1994) and behavioral effects of regional sexual transformation (Ferveur et al. 1995; O'Dell et al. 1995). Such GAL4 lines can also selectively trap enhancers of a complex gene, as exploited by Vincent et al. (1994) to separate temporal elements of *Ubx* regulation.

GAL4 has the additional advantage of temperature sensitivity; it is more active at 29°C (closer to yeast's optimal growth temperature) than at 18°C. On the other hand, it has the disadvantage that some GAL4 strains show inconsistent patterns of expression or sensitivity to changes in genetic background. These problems can be controlled by assessing expression patterns in a suitable number of individuals for each strain and by keeping genetic background consistent.

## CELL ABLATIONS

Promoter fusions and GAL4 enhancer traps have the potential to drive genetic cell ablations—autonomous expression of cytotoxic gene products. Should such a technique be perfected, it might overcome a nagging sense of inferiority that fly people experience when listening to the nematode litany of "advantages of the organism." (Another advantage is the ability to freeze the animals in liquid nitrogen, a technique that is equally possible in flies and worms, but with somewhat different outcomes.) Diphtheria toxin and ricin have been expressed under tissue-specific and temporal control (Moffat et al. 1992; Sentry et al. 1993), but such efforts have generally ended up on the rocks due to the problem of leaky expression of toxin. (It doesn't take much.) One effort that shows promise is the light chain of tetanus toxin which is capable of blocking synaptic transmission in neurons (Sweeney et al. 1995).

# CHAPTER 7

# You're on Your Own

You have now completed the training and hazing process and are ready to go out into the world and begin pushing flies in earnest. It is hoped that by this time you have learned the principles at an intellectual level, but there is no substitute for doing crosses yourself with real flies in real time. That is the only way to get a proper feel for how it works and for its rhythms and pitfalls.

As a last reminder, there are several points that bear repeating and remembering as you make your way through the maze of planning and executing genetic schemes:

• You will never overestimate the number of flies needed for a multi-generational scheme. Since it hurts to start over again after 3 or 4 months, even a 10-fold excess over what you calculate as a minimum is not out of line for large schemes with many generations.

• If there are two ways to construct a strain, do both. Many schemes look great on paper but fail miserably (and sometimes unaccountably) in the bottle and you won't know for a couple of months. This step saves you from having to start over.

• Arrange your crosses to compensate for non-virginity wherever possible. This is especially important if your social life should suddenly become complicated and you miss the odd virgin collection.

• Run small-scale pilots before undertaking large crosses. This permits you to test your stocks and avoid time-wasting failures.

• Don't be discouraged if things don't work at first. You will acquire a feel for fly pushing with time. Moreover, the flies frequently require you to do an apprenticeship on any important project—they won't start to perform until they are certain you are serious.

And the final exhortation is best expressed by Shakespeare in *King Lear*:

*The wren goes to't, and the small gilded fly*
*Does lecher in my sight.*
*Let copulation thrive...*

# Solutions to Problems

## SOLUTION 1

<table>
<tr><td>Normal</td><td></td><td>Attached-X</td><td></td><td>Attached-X with Y</td></tr>
</table>

**Normal**

♂   ♀

$$\frac{w}{Y} \times \frac{y}{y}$$

↓

♂   ♀

$$\frac{y}{Y} \quad \frac{y}{w}$$

vs.

Sons receive one
of mother's $X$s
and father's $Y$,
daughters receive
father's $X$

**Attached-X**

♂   ☿

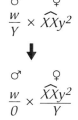

$$\frac{w}{Y} \times \widehat{XX}y^2$$

↓

♂   ♀

$$\frac{w}{0} \times \frac{\widehat{XX}y^2}{Y}$$

Sons receive
father's $X$,
daughters receive
mother's attached-$X$
and father's $Y$,
producing $X0$
sterile sons

vs.
when the
mother
also carries
a $Y$

**Attached-X with Y**

♂   ☿

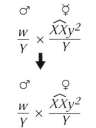

$$\frac{w}{Y} \times \frac{\widehat{XX}y^2}{Y}$$

↓

♂   ♀

$$\frac{w}{Y} \times \frac{\widehat{XX}y^2}{Y}$$

Sons and
daughters both
receive $Y$, making
sons fertile and
having no effect
on daughters

## SOLUTION 2

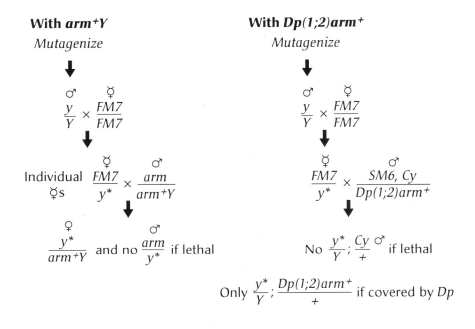

**With *arm+Y***

*Mutagenize*

↓

♂          ♀
$\dfrac{y}{Y}$  ×  $\dfrac{FM7}{FM7}$

↓

♀                    ♂
Individual  $\dfrac{FM7}{y^*}$  ×  $\dfrac{arm}{arm^+Y}$
♀s

↓

♀                              ♂
$\dfrac{y^*}{arm^+Y}$  and no  $\dfrac{arm}{y^*}$  if lethal

**With *Dp(1;2)arm+***

*Mutagenize*

↓

♂          ♀
$\dfrac{y}{Y}$  ×  $\dfrac{FM7}{FM7}$

↓

♀              ♂
$\dfrac{FM7}{y^*}$  ×  $\dfrac{SM6,\ Cy}{Dp(1;2)arm^+}$

↓

No  $\dfrac{y^*}{Y};\dfrac{Cy}{+}$ ♂  if lethal

Only  $\dfrac{y^*}{Y};\dfrac{Dp(1;2)arm^+}{+}$  if covered by *Dp*

## SOLUTION 3

You are mutagenizing males hemizygous for an $X$, so any $X$-linked lethals in the stock would not appear in the adult males.

## SOLUTION 4

$$\sigma^{\!\!\!\!\!\!\!\!\!\!\!\!\!'} \qquad \qquad \qquad \raisebox{0.3em}{$\female$}$$
$$\frac{w}{Y};\ w^{+?} \quad \times \quad \frac{w}{w};\ \frac{In(2LR)O,Cy}{Sco};\ \frac{Sb}{TM6,\ Ubx}$$

⬇ If on the $X$, no male progeny will be $w^+$

$$\sigma^{\!\!\!\!\!\!\!\!\!\!\!\!\!'} \qquad \qquad \raisebox{0.3em}{$\female$}$$
$$\frac{w}{Y};\ \frac{Cy;\ Sb}{w^{+?}} \quad \times \quad \frac{w}{w}$$

⬇

if on *2nd* chromosome, all $w^+$ will be $Cy^+$,
if on *3rd* chromosome, all $w^+$ will be $Sb^+$,
if on *4th* chromosome, no correlation with $Cy$ or $Sb$

To balance it and test for homozygous viability (assuming hypothetically it's on chromosome *2*):

$$\sigma^{\!\!\!\!\!\!\!\!\!\!\!\!\!'} \qquad \qquad \qquad \raisebox{0.3em}{$\female$}$$
$$\frac{w}{Y};\ \frac{w^{+?}}{+} \quad \times \quad \frac{w}{w};\ \frac{In(2LR)O,Cy}{Sco}$$

↙

$$\sigma^{\!\!\!\!\!\!\!\!\!\!\!\!\!'} \qquad \qquad \qquad \raisebox{0.3em}{$\female$}$$
$$\frac{w}{Y};\ \frac{w^+}{Sco} \quad \times \quad \frac{w}{w};\ \frac{In(2LR)O,Cy}{w^+}$$

↙ ↘

$$\sigma^{\!\!\!\!\!\!\!\!\!\!\!\!\!'} \qquad \qquad \qquad \sigma^{\!\!\!\!\!\!\!\!\!\!\!\!\!'}\ \&\ \raisebox{0.3em}{$\female$}$$
$$\frac{w}{Y};\ \frac{w^+}{w^+} \quad \text{and} \quad w;\ \frac{In(2LR)O,Cy}{w^+}$$

↙

Viability test        Balanced stock

# SOLUTION 5

$$Birm2 \quad \frac{[P][P][P][P][P]...}{[P][P][P][P][P]...} \quad \times \quad \frac{Sb\Delta 2\text{-}3}{TM3}$$

↙

$$\text{♂} \quad \frac{[P][P][P][P][P]...}{+} \; ; \; \frac{Sb\Delta 2\text{-}3}{+} \quad \times \quad \frac{TM6, Ubx}{Sb} \; \text{♀}$$

↙

$$\text{Individual ♂} \quad \frac{[P]?}{TM6, Ubx} \quad \times \quad \frac{TM6B, D}{cno} \; \text{♀}$$

↙                    ↘

$$\frac{[P]?}{cno} \quad \text{and} \quad \frac{[P]?}{TM6B, D}$$

Complementation        Recover new allele
test                   in balanced stock

## SOLUTION 6

When both $T(Y;A)$s have breakpoints in the same $Y$ arm, then duplications and deletions look just like euploids: all have $y^+$ and $B^S$.

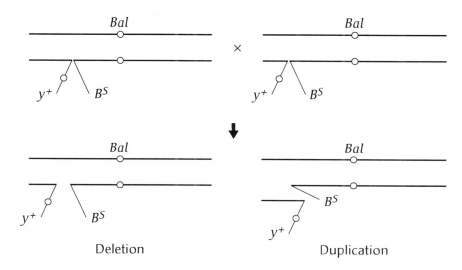

When the breakpoints are in different $Y$ arms, but one has lost $B^S$, as is the case with many of these stocks, then duplications and deletions are distinguishable:

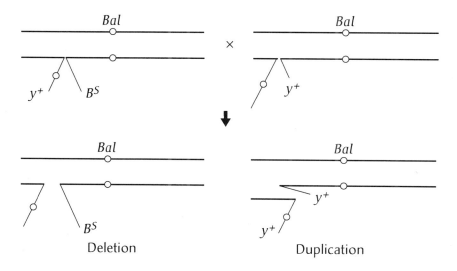

## SOLUTION 7

$$\frac{v\ x?}{FM7} \times \frac{yf}{Y}$$ 

x? symbolizes the new mutation introduced from ♀ in case it affects fertility

↓

$$\frac{v\ x?}{yf} \times \frac{FM7}{Y}$$

↓

Individual ♂ progeny × $\frac{\widehat{XX}y^2}{Y}$ to start new stock from each

## SOLUTION 8

$$\frac{w}{Y} ; \frac{P[w^+\text{-}lacZ]}{P[w^+\text{-}lacZ]} \times \frac{w}{w} ; \frac{TM6,\ Ubx}{h}$$

(for construction of this stock, see below)

↓

$$\frac{w}{w} ; \frac{P[w^+\text{-}lacZ]}{h} \times \frac{w}{Y} ; \frac{TM3,\ Ser}{Sb}$$

↙

Individual ♂   $$\frac{w}{Y} ; \frac{P[w^+\text{-}lacZ]\ h?}{TM3,\ Ser} \times \frac{w}{w} ; \frac{TM6,\ Ubx}{h}$$

↙   ↘

$$\frac{w}{Y} ; \frac{P[w^+\text{-}lacZ]\ h?}{h}$$   and   ♂ & ♀  $$w; \frac{TM6,\ Ubx}{P[w^+\text{-}lacZ]\ h}$$

None of this class of progeny will survive if *h* is now linked to $w^+$

Recover as balanced stock

$$\frac{w}{w} ; \frac{TM3,\ Ser}{Sb} \times \frac{TM6,\ Ubx}{h}$$

↓

$$\frac{w}{Y} ; \frac{TM3,\ Ser}{h} \times \frac{w}{w} ; \frac{TM6,\ Ubx}{Sb}$$

$$w; \frac{TM6,\ Ubx}{h}$$

## SOLUTION 9

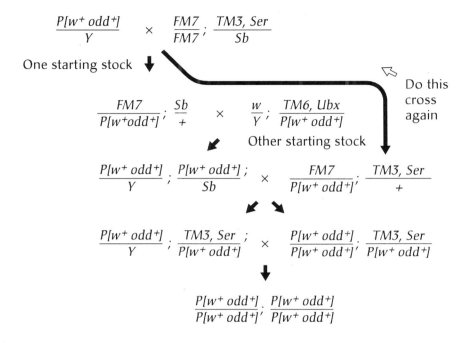

$$\frac{P[w^+\ odd^+]}{Y} \quad \times \quad \frac{FM7}{FM7}\ ;\ \frac{TM3,\ Ser}{Sb}$$

One starting stock ↓

$$\frac{FM7}{P[w^+odd^+]}\ ;\ \frac{Sb}{+} \quad \times \quad \frac{w}{Y}\ ;\ \frac{TM6,\ Ubx}{P[w^+\ odd^+]}$$

Other starting stock

Do this
cross
again

$$\frac{P[w^+\ odd^+]}{Y}\ ;\ \frac{P[w^+\ odd^+]}{Sb}\ ; \quad \times \quad \frac{FM7}{P[w^+\ odd^+]}\ ;\ \frac{TM3,\ Ser}{+}$$

$$\frac{P[w^+\ odd^+]}{Y}\ ;\ \frac{TM3,\ Ser}{P[w^+\ odd^+]}\ ; \quad \times \quad \frac{P[w^+\ odd^+]}{P[w^+\ odd^+]}\ ;\ \frac{TM3,\ Ser}{P[w^+\ odd^+]}$$

$$\frac{P[w^+\ odd^+]}{P[w^+\ odd^+]}\ ;\ \frac{P[w^+\ odd^+]}{P[w^+\ odd^+]}$$

## SOLUTION 10

$$\frac{Cbx}{TM8,\ Sb} \quad \times \quad \frac{TM3,\ Ser}{Sb}$$

↓

Look for loss
of dominant
phenotype

$$\frac{TM3,\ Ser}{Cbx^*} \quad \times \quad \frac{TM8,\ Sb}{D}$$   Balancer, dominant stock

$$\frac{TM8,\ Sb}{Cbx^*} \quad \times \quad \frac{TM8,\ Sb}{Cbx^*}$$

## SOLUTION 11

### On the $X$:

Mutagenize

↘ $\dfrac{y}{Y}$ × $\dfrac{\widehat{XX}y^2}{Y}$ ; $\dfrac{In(2LR)O,Cy}{Sco}$

↓

$\dfrac{y^*}{Y}$ ; $\dfrac{Sco}{+}$

### On chromosome 3:

Mutagenize

↘ $\dfrac{e}{e}$ × $\dfrac{TM6B, D}{Sb}$

↘

Handy stock to have    $\dfrac{In(2LR)O,Cy}{Sco}$ ; $\dfrac{TM6, Ubx}{Sb}$ × $\dfrac{e^*}{TM6B, D}$

↙ ↓

$\dfrac{In(2LR)O,Cy}{+}$ ; $\dfrac{TM6B, D}{Sb}$ × $\dfrac{Sco}{+}$ ; $\dfrac{e^*}{TM6, Ubx}$

↙ ↘

$\dfrac{Sco}{In(2LR)O,Cy}$ ; $\dfrac{TM6B, D}{e^*}$ × $\dfrac{Sco}{In(2LR)O,Cy}$ ; $\dfrac{TM6B, D}{e^*}$

↓

$\dfrac{Sco}{In(2LR)O,Cy}$ ; $\dfrac{e^*}{e^*}$

Can't be done on chromosome 2 because *Sco* is homozygous lethal.

# SOLUTION 12

The final, mosaic–producing cross will consist of the following:

$$\frac{Hk}{Hk'} ; \frac{ca^{nd}}{ca^{nd}} \quad \times \quad \frac{y}{Y}$$

$$\downarrow$$

$$\frac{Hk}{y} ; \frac{ca^{nd}}{+} \quad \text{Potential mosaics}$$

To get there:

$$\frac{FM7}{FM7} \quad \times \quad \frac{TM3, Ser}{Sb}$$

$$\downarrow \qquad \searrow$$

$$\frac{Hk}{Hk} \times \frac{FM7}{Y} ; \frac{TM3, Ser}{Sb} \qquad \frac{FM7}{+} ; \frac{Sb}{+} \times \frac{TM6, Ubx}{ca^{nd}}$$

$$\downarrow \qquad\qquad\qquad\qquad\qquad \downarrow$$

$$\frac{FM7}{Hk} ; \frac{TM3, Ser}{+} \qquad \times \qquad \frac{FM7}{Y} ; \frac{Sb}{ca^{nd}}$$

$$\downarrow$$

$$\frac{FM7}{Hk} ; \frac{TM3, Ser}{ca^{nd}} \quad \times \quad \frac{Hk}{Y} ; \frac{TM3, Ser}{ca^{nd}}$$

$$\downarrow$$

$$\frac{Hk}{Hk'} ; \frac{ca^{nd}}{ca^{nd}} \quad \text{and} \quad Hk ; \frac{TM3, Ser}{ca^{nd}} \qquad \text{♂ \& ♀}$$

For mosaics       For keeping the stock

# Glossary

**amorph** a mutation that functionally inactivates a gene by producing either no product or a nonfunctional product (synonym: null allele)

**aneuploidy** individual, gamete, or cell that contains too little or too much genetic material

**antimorph** mutation that shows anomalous complementation such that the individuals are more severely affected when heterozygous with another mutation than when homozygous

**balancer** chromosome containing multiple inversions and markers that facilitate crossing schemes by their ease of detection and also by their suppression of recombination between homologs

**complementation** genetic test of allelism in which one mutation is placed heterozygous with another and scored for normal (complementing) vs. abnormal (noncomplementing) phenotype

**compound chromosome** rearrangement in which both homologous arms of a chromosome are attached to the same centromere (also called "attached")

**deficiency** rearrangement in which a piece of a chromosome is excised and the remaining large pieces reattached (synonym: deletion)

**deletion** see deficiency

**diploid** containing the normal complement, two sets, of chromosomes (adjective: diplo-)

**distal** toward the tip of a chromosome arm

**duplication** rearrangement in which an extra piece of chromosome is attached or inserted into an ectopic site

**enhancer** 1) mutation or genetic variant at one locus that exacerbates the phenotype of a mutation at another locus; 2) regulatory DNA sequence that influences transcription of nearby gene(s)

**enhancer-trap** technique in which a gene introduced into an ectopic chromosomal site is expressed in a restricted pattern due to its proximity to endogenous enhancers; also refers to the strain carrying such an insertion

**euploid** individual, gamete, or cell containing its appropriate and normal amount of genetic material

**haploid** containing a single set of chromosomes (adjective: haplo-)

**haplo-insufficient** locus or chromosomal region in which a single dose of wild-type does not produce a normal phenotype

**hemizygous** chromosome or chromosomal region present in only one dose

**hypermorph** mutation in which the gene product is produced at higher levels than normal or is more active than normal

**hyperploid** containing more than the normal amount of genetic material

**hypomorph** mutation in which the gene product is produced at lower levels than normal or is less active than normal

**insertion** ectopic presence of a DNA sequence or chromosomal region

**inversion** rearrangement in which part of the normal sequence of a chromosome is reversed

**metacentric** chromosome (or rearrangement) in which the centromere is flanked on both sides by major chromosome arms

**mosaic** individual whose cells are not all of the same genotype

**neomorph** mutation in which the gene product functions as if performing a new function, as opposed to no function (amorph), too little function (hypomorph), or too much function (hypermorph)

**null** see amorph

**proximal** toward the centromere

**suppressor** mutation or genetic variant at one locus that rescues or mitigates the phenotype of a mutation at another locus

**translocation** rearrangement in which two different chromosomes are broken and re-joined such that they have exchanged pieces

**transposition** rearrangement in which a piece of a chromosome is excised and reinserted elsewhere in the same chromosome

**triploid** individual or cell containing three sets of chromosomes

# APPENDIX
# Fly Resources

## BOOKS

Ashburner, M. (1989) *Drosophila: A laboratory handbook.* Cold Spring Harbor Laboratory Press: Cold Spring Harbor.
> The Talmud of fly genetics with referenced information on all aspects of fly genetics, biology, and molecular biology.

Goldstein, L.S.B. and Fyrberg, E.A. (1994) *Drosophila melanogaster: Practical Uses in Cell and Molecular Biology. Methods in Cell Biology.* Academic Press: San Diego.
> Manual of techniques, main emphasis on molecular biology and biochemistry.

Lindsley, D.L. and Zimm, G.G. (1992) *The Genome of Drosophila melanogaster.* Academic Press: San Diego.
> Also known as the "Red Book," with information on loci, phenotypes, rearrangements, and the general foundation of fly genetic information.

## FLYBASE

A computerized database for information on fly genetics and molecular biology can be found at the Web site

http://morgan.harvard.edu/

where information from Lindsley and Zimm is available and updated, as well as extensive compendia on extant clones, sequences, molecular mapping, transposons, and so on. Also contains a directory of Drosophila researchers, a directory of meetings, techniques, images, and the usual array of Web site features.

A descriptive excerpt from FlyBase:

FlyBase is a database of genetic and molecular data for Drosophila. You can access FlyBase data by using a World-Wide Web (WWW) browser, the Internet Gopher, anonymous ftp, or the GopherMail email server.

These are the URLs you can use to access FlyBase using the Netscape Navigator, Mosaic, lynx, or another WWW browser:

http://morgan.harvard.edu/
http://flybase.bio.indiana.edu:82/
http://www.embl-ebi.ac.uk/flybase
http://www.angis.su.oz.au:7081/
http://shigen.lab.nig.ac.jp:7081/

Some FlyBase data, merged with data from the Berkeley Drosophila Genome Project (BDGP), is available as the Encyclopaedia of Drosophila, a collaborative effort of the BDGP and FlyBase. Version 3.0, for the WWW, is available via the BDGP home page at

http://fruitfly.berkeley.edu.

Version 2.0 is available on CD-ROM; inquire to

eofd-sales@morgan.harvard.edu.

You can reach the FlyBase gopher+ server with any gopher client at:

flybase.bio.indiana.edu
www.embl-ebi.ac.uk
gopher.angis.su.oz.au
shigen.lab.nig.ac.jp

You can reach the anonymous ftp server at

flybase.bio.indiana.edu.

Type the user name anonymous when it asks for your login name, and please enter your full email address as the password. All of the FlyBase files are in a directory called "flybase". Gopher clients for a variety of computers are in a directory called util/gopher.

Information about using FlyBase's GopherMail services will be emailed to you if you send a message containing the single word "help" in its subject or message body to

flybase-gopher@flybase.bio.indiana.edu

If you do not have Internet access, we suggest you talk to your local computer experts. FlyBase periodically publishes extracts of its data as special issues of the Drosophila Information Service (DIS).

FlyBase includes the following:

A bibliography of over 82,000 Drosophila citations
An address book of over 5,000 Drosophila researchers
Information on more than 32,000 alleles of nearly 10,000 genes
Descriptions of over 12,000 chromosomal aberrations
Drosophila genetic map information
Information on the functions of gene products
Lists of stock center and private lab Drosophila stocks
A listing of over 9,000 nucleic and over 3,000 protein sequence accession
    numbers
Lists of over 7,000 genomic clones
Allied databases
Berkeley Drosophila Genome Project data
European Drosophila Genome Project data
The bionet.drosophila archives
Drosophila Images
Wild type Drosophila strains and chromosomes

## STOCK CENTERS

Bloomington, Indiana --
Dept. of Biology
Indiana University
Bloomington, IN 47405
812-855-5782
812-855-5783 (answering machine)
FAX 812-855-6705
e-mail: matthewk@indiana.edu

Bowling Green, Ohio
419-372-2332
FAX 419-372-2024

The above excerpt was reprinted with permission from the FlyBase consortium.

# References

Ambrosio, L., Mahowald, A.P., and Perrimon, N. 1989. The *Drosophila raf* homologue is required for *torso* function. *Nature* **342**: 288–291.

Arnold, J. and Kankel, D.R. 1981. Fate mapping multi-focus phenotypes. *Genetics* **99**: 211–229.

Ashburner, M. 1989. *Drosophila: A laboratory handbook.* Cold Spring Harbor Laboratory Press, Cold Spring Harbor, New York.

Avery, L. and Wasserman, S. 1992. Ordering gene function: The interpretation of epistasis in regulatory hierarchies. *Trends Genet.* **8**: 312–316.

Baker, B.S. 1975. Paternal loss (*pal*): A meiotic mutant in *Drosophila melanogaster* causing loss of paternal chromosomes. *Genetics* **80**: 267–296.

Ballinger, D.G. and Benzer, S. 1989. Targeted gene mutations in *Drosophila*. *Proc. Natl. Acad. Sci.* **86**: 9402–9406.

Bell, L.R., Horabin, J.I., Schedl, P., and Cline, T.W. 1991. Positive autoregulation of sex-lethal by alternative splicing maintains the female determined state in *Drosophila*. *Cell* **65**: 229–239.

Bellen, H.J., O'Kane, C.J., Wilson, C., Grossniklaus, U., Pearson, R.K., and Gehring, W.J. 1989. P-element-mediated enhancer detection: A versatile method to study development in *Drosophila*. *Genes Dev.* **3**: 1288–1300.

Belote, J.M. and Baker, B.S. 1982. Sex determination in *Drosophila melanogaster*: Analysis of transformer-2, a sex-transforming locus. *Proc. Natl. Acad. Sci.* **79**: 1568–1572.

Bier, E., Vaessin, H., Shepherd, S., Lee, K., McCall, K., Barbel, S., Ackerman, L., Carretto, R., Uemura, T., and Grell, E. 1989. Searching for pattern and mutation in the *Drosophila* genome with a P-lacZ vector. *Genes Dev.* **3**: 1273–1287.

Biggs, W.H. III, Zavitz, K.H., Dickson, B., van der Straten, A., Brunner, D., Hafen, E., and Zipursky, S.L. 1994. The *Drosophila* rolled locus encodes a MAP kinase required in the sevenless signal transduction pathway. *EMBO J.* **13**: 1628–1635.

Bingham, P.M., Kidwell, M.G., and Rubin, G.M. 1982. The molecular basis of P-M hybrid dysgenesis: The role of the P-element, a P-strain-specific transposon family. *Cell* **29**: 995–1004.

Botas, J., Moscoso del Prado, J., and García-Bellido, A. 1982. Gene-dose titration analysis in the search of trans-regulatory genes in *Drosophila*. *EMBO J.* **1**: 307–310.

**143**

Bownes, M. and Sang, J.H. 1974. Experimental manipulations of early *Drosophila* embryos. I. Adult and embryonic defects resulting from microcautery at nuclear multiplication and blastoderm stages. *J. Embryol. Exp. Morphol.* **32**: 253–272.

Brand, A.H. and Perrimon, N. 1993. Targeted gene expression as a means of altering cell fates and generating dominant phenotypes. *Development* **118**: 401–415.

———. 1994. Raf acts downstream of the EGF receptor to determine dorsoventral polarity during *Drosophila* oogenesis. *Genes Dev.* **8**: 629–639.

Brunner, D., Oellers, N., Szabad, J., Biggs, W.H., III, Zipursky, S.L., and Hafen, E. 1994. A gain-of-function mutation in *Drosophila* MAP kinase activates multiple receptor tyrosine kinase signaling pathways. *Cell* **76**: 875–888.

Bryant, P.J. and Schneiderman, H.A. 1969. Cell lineage, growth, and determination in the imaginal leg discs of *Drosophila melanogaster*. *Dev. Biol.* **20**: 263–290.

Byers, D., Davis, R.L., and Kiger, J.A., Jr. 1981. Defect in cyclic AMP due to the *dunce* mutation of learning in *Drosophila melanogaster*. *Nature* **289**: 79–81.

Cagan, R.L. and Ready, D.F. 1989. Notch is required for successive cell decisions in the developing *Drosophila* retina. *Genes Dev.* **3**: 1099–1112.

Carlson, E.A. 1971. A genetic analysis of the *rudimentary* locus of *Drosophila melanogaster*. *Genet. Res.* **17**: 53–81.

Cline, T.W. 1978. Two closely linked mutations in *Drosophila melanogaster* that are lethal to opposite sexes and interact with daughterless. *Genetics* **90**: 683–698.

———. 1984. Autoregulatory functioning of a *Drosophila* gene product that establishes and maintains the sexually determined state. *Genetics* **107**: 231–277.

Cooley, L., Kelley, R., and Spradling, A.C. 1988. Insertional mutagenesis of the *Drosophila* genome with single P-elements. *Science* **239**: 1121–1128.

Craymer, L. 1981. Techniques for manipulating chromosomal rearrangements and their application to *Drosophila melanogaster*. I. Pericentric inversions. *Genetics* **99**: 75–97.

———. 1984. Techniques for manipulating chromosomal rearrangements and their application to *Drosophila melanogaster*. II. Translocations. *Genetics* **108**: 573–587.

Dalby, B., Pereira, A.J., and Goldstein, L.S. 1995. An inverse PCR screen for the detection of P element insertions in cloned genomic intervals in *Drosophila melanogaster*. *Genetics* **139**: 757–766.

Davis, I., Girdham, C.H., and O'Farrell, P.H. 1995. A nuclear GFP that marks nuclei in living *Drosophila* embryos: Maternal supply overcomes a delay in the appearance of zygotic fluorescence. *Dev. Biol.* **170**: 726–729.

Doe, C.Q., Smouse, D., and Goodman, C.S. 1988. Control of neuronal fate by the *Drosophila* segmentation gene even-skipped. *Nature* **333**: 376–378.

Dolph, P.J., Ranganathan, R., Colley, N.J., Hardy, R.W., Socolich, M., and Zuker, C.S. 1993. Arrestin function in inactivation of G protein-coupled receptor rhodopsin in vivo. *Science* **260**: 1910–1916.

Engels, W.R., Johnson-Schlitz, D.M., Eggleston, W.B., and Sved, J. 1990. High-frequency P-element loss in *Drosophila* is homolog dependent. *Cell* **62**:

515–525.

Ferveur, J.-F., Störtkuhl, K., Stocker, R.F., and Greenspan, R.J. 1995. Genetic feminization of brain structures and changed sexual orientation in male *Drosophila melanogaster*. *Science* **267**: 902–905.

Flanagan, J.R. 1977. A method for fate mapping foci of lethal and behavioral mutants in *Drosophila melanogaster*. *Genetics* **85**: 587–607.

Gailey, D.A., Bordne, D.L., Vallés, A.M., Hall, J.C., and White, K. 1987. Construction of an unstable *Ring-X* chromosome bearing the autosomal gene dopa decarboxylase in *Drosophila melanogaster* and analysis of *Ddc* mosaics. *Genetics* **115**: 305–311.

García-Bellido, A. and Merriam, J.R. 1969. Cell lineage of the imaginal discs in *Drosophila* gynandromorphs. *J. Exp. Zool.* **170**: 61–75.

García-Bellido, A., Ripoll, P., and Morata, G. 1973. Developmental compartmentalization of the wing disc of *Drosophila*. *Nat. New Biol.* **245**: 251–253.

Gergen, J.P. and Wieschaus, E. 1985. The localized requirements for a gene affecting segmentation in *Drosophila:* Analysis of larvae mosaic for *runt*. *Dev. Biol.* **109**: 321–335.

————. 1986. Localized requirements for gene activity in segmentation of *Drosophila* embryos: Analysis of *armadillo, fused, giant* and *unpaired* mutations in mosaic embryos. *Roux's Arch. Dev. Biol.* **195**: 49–62.

Gloor, G.B., Nassif, N.A., Johnson-Schlitz, D.M., Preston, C.R., and Engels, W.R. 1991. Targeted gene replacement in *Drosophila* via P element-induced gap repair. *Science* **253**: 1110–1117.

Goldstein, L.S.B. and Fyrberg, E.A., eds. 1994. *Drosophila melanogaster:* Practical uses in cell and molecular biology. *Methods in cell biology*, vol. 44. Academic Press, San Diego.

Golic, K.G. 1991. Site-specific recombination between homologous chromosomes in *Drosophila*. *Science* **252**: 958–961.

————. 1994. Local transposition of P elements in *Drosophila melanogaster* and recombination between duplicated elements using a site-specific recombinase. *Genetics* **137**: 551–563.

Golic, K.G. and Lindquist, S. 1989. The FLP recombinase of yeast catalyzes site-specific recombination in the *Drosophila* genome. *Cell* **59**: 499–509.

Goodwin, S.F., DelVecchio, M., Tully, T., and Kaiser, K. 1993. Behavior of *Drosophila* mutant for a regulatory sub-unit of cAMP-dependent protein kinase. *J. Neurogenet.* **8**: 232.

Greenspan, R.J. 1980. Mutations of choline acetyltransferase and associated neural defects in *Drosophila melanogaster*. *J. Comp. Physiol.* **137**: 83–92.

————. 1990. The emergence of neurogenetics. *Semin. Neurosci.* **2**: 145–157.

Greenspan, R.J., Finn, J.A., and Hall, J.C. 1980. Acetylcholinesterase mutants in *Drosophila* and their effects on the structure and function of the central nervous system. *J. Comp. Neurol.* **189**: 741–774.

Hall, J.C. 1977. Portions of the central nervous system controlling reproductive behavior in *Drosophila melanogaster*. *Behav. Genet.* **7**: 291–312.

———. 1979. Control of male reproductive behavior by the central nervous system of *Drosophila:* Dissection of a courtship pathway by genetic mosaics. *Genetics* **92**: 437–457.

———. 1994. Pleiotropy of behavioral genes. In *Flexibility and constraint in behavioral systems* (ed. Greenspan, R.J. and Kyriacou, C.P.), pp. 15–27. John Wiley, New York.

Hall, J.C. and Kankel, D.R. 1976. Genetics of acetylcholinesterase in *Drosophila melanogaster*. *Genetics* **83**: 517–535.

Hall, J.C., Gelbart, W.M., and Kankel, D.R. 1976. Mosaic system. In *The genetics and biology of* Drosophila (ed. Ashburner, M. and Novitski, E.), vol. 1a, pp. 265–314. Academic Press, New York.

Hamblen, M., Zehring, W.A., Kyriacou, C.P., Reddy, P., Yu, Q., Wheeler, D.A., Zwiebel, L.J., Konopka, R.J., Rosbash, M., and Hall, J.C. 1986. Germ-line transformation involving DNA from the *period* locus in *Drosophila melanogaster:* Overlapping genomic fragments that restore circadian and ultradian rhythmicity to *per⁰* and *per⁻* mutants. *J. Neurogenet.* **3**: 249–291.

Hardy, R.W. 1975. The influence of chromosome content on the size and shape of sperm heads in *Drosophila melanogaster* and the demonstration of chromosome loss during spermiogenesis. *Genetics* **79**: 231–264.

Harris, W.A., Stark, W.S., and Walker, J.A. 1976. Genetic dissection of the photoreceptor system in the compound eye of *Drosophila melanogaster*. *J. Physiol.* **256**: 415–439.

Hilliker, A.J. 1976. Genetic analysis of the centromeric heterochromatin of chromosome 2 of *Drosophila melanogaster:* Deficiency mapping of EMS-induced lethal complementation groups. *Genetics* **83**: 765–782.

Hodgetts, R.B. 1975. The response of dopa decarboxylase activity to variations in gene dosage in *Drosophila:* A possible location of the structural gene. *Genetics* **79**: 45–54.

Hoppe, P. and Greenspan, R.J. 1986. Local function of the Notch gene for embryonic ectodermal pathway choice in *Drosophila*. *Cell* **46**: 773–783.

———. 1990. The *Notch* locus of *Drosophila* is required in epidermal cells for epidermal development. *Development* **109**: 875–885.

Janning, W. 1978. Gynandromorph fate maps in *Drosophila*. In *Genetic mosaics and cell differentiation. Results and problems in cell differentiation* (ed. Gehring, W.J.), vol. 9, pp. 1–28. Springer-Verlag, New York.

Kaiser, K. and Goodwin, S.F. 1990. "Site-selected" transposon mutagenesis of *Drosophila*. *Proc. Natl. Acad. Sci.* **87**: 1686–1690.

Kankel, D.R. and Hall, J.C. 1976. Fate mapping of nervous system and other internal tissues in genetic mosaics of *Drosophila melanogaster*. *Dev. Biol.* **48**: 1–24.

Keeler, K.J., Dray, T., Penney, J.E., and Gloor, G.B. 1996. Gene targeting of a plasmid-borne sequence to a double-strand break in *Drosophila melanogaster*. *Mol. Cell Biol.* **16**: 522–528.

Kelley, M.R., Kidd, S., Deutsch, W.A., and Young, M.W. 1987. Mutations altering the structure of epidermal growth factor-like coding sequences at the *Drosophila* Notch locus. *Cell* **51**: 539–548.

Kernan, M.J., Kuroda, M.I., Kreber, R., Baker, B.S., and Ganetzky, G. 1991. *nap*ts, a mutation affecting sodium channel activity in *Drosophila*, is an allele of *mle*, a regulator of X chromosome transcription. *Cell* **66**: 949–959.

Kiger, J.A., Jr. and Golanty, E. 1977. A cytogenetic analysis of cyclic nucleotide phosphodiesterase activities in *Drosophila. Genetics* **85**: 609–622.

Klingler, M., Erdelyi, M., Szabad, J., and Nüsslein-Volhard, C. 1988. Function of torso in determining the terminal anlagen of the *Drosophila* embryo. *Nature* **335**: 275–277.

Lawrence, P.A. 1982. Cell lineage of the thoracic muscles of *Drosophila. Cell* **29**: 493–503.

Lawrence, P.A. and Green, S.M. 1979. Cell lineage in the developing retina of *Drosophila. Dev. Biol.* **71**: 142–152.

Lawrence, P.A. and Johnston, P. 1986. Observations on the cell lineage of internal organs. *J. Exp. Embryol. Exp. Morphol.* **91**: 251–266.

Levine, M., Hafen, E., Garber, R.L., and Gehring, W.J. 1983. Spatial distribution of *Antennapedia* transcripts during *Drosophila* development. *EMBO J.* **2**: 2037–2046.

Lewis, E.B. 1963. Genes and developmental pathways. *Am. Zool.* **3**: 33–56.

———. 1985. Regulation of genes in the Bithorax complex in *Drosophila. Cold Spring Harbor Symp. Quant. Biol.* **50**: 155–164.

Lindsley, D.L. and Zimm, G.G. 1992. *The genome of* Drosophila melanogaster. Academic Press, San Diego.

Lindsley, D.L., Sandler, L., Baker, B.S., Carpenter, A.T.C., Denell, R.F., Hall, J.C., Jacobs, P.A., Miklos, G.L.G., Davis, B.K., Gethmann, R.C., Hardy, R.W., Hessler, A., Miller, S.M., Nozawa, H., Parry, D.M., and Gould-Somero, M. 1972. Segmental aneuploidy and the genetic gross structure of the *Drosophila* genome. *Genetics* **71**: 157–184.

Lyman, D. and Young, M.W. 1993. Further evidence for function of the *Drosophila* Notch protein as a transmembrane receptor. *Proc. Natl. Acad. Sci.* **90**: 10395–10399.

Lyttle, T.W. 1984. Chromosomal control of fertility in *Drosophila melanogaster*. I. Rescue of T(Y;A)/bb[l-158] male sterility by chromosome rearrangement. *Genetics* **106**: 423–434.

Mather, K. 1951. *The measurement of linkage in heredity*, 2nd edition. Methuen, London.

Merrill, P.T., Sweeton, D., and Wieschaus, E. 1988. Requirements for autosomal gene activity during precellular stages of *Drosophila melanogaster. Development* **104**: 495–509.

Moffat, K.G., Gould, J.H., Smith, H.K., and O'Kane, C.J. 1992. Inducible cell ablation in *Drosophila* by cold-sensitive ricin A chain. *Development* **114**: 681–687.

Morata, G. and García-Bellido, A. 1976. Developmental analysis of some mutants of the bithorax system of *Drosophila. Roux's Arch. Dev. Biol.* **179**: 125–143.

Morata, G. and Lawrence, P.A. 1975. Control of compartment development by the *engrailed* gene in *Drosophila. Nature* **255**: 614–617.

Morata, G. and Ripoll, P. 1975. Minutes: Mutants of *Drosophila* autonomously affecting cell division rate. *Dev. Biol.* **42**: 211–221.

Muller, H.J. 1918. Genetic variability, twin hybrids and constant hybrids, in a case of balanced lethal factors. *Genetics* **3**: 422–499.

O'Dell, K.M., Armstrong, J.D., Yang, M.Y., and Kaiser, K. 1995. Functional dissection of the *Drosophila* mushroom bodies by selective feminization of genetically defined subcompartments. *Neuron* **15**: 55–61.

O'Kane, C. and Gehring, W.J. 1987. Detection in situ of genomic regulatory elements in *Drosophila. Proc. Natl. Acad. Sci.* **84**: 9123–9127.

Pak, W.L., Ostroy, S.E., Deland, M.C., and Wu, C.F. 1980. Photoreceptor mutant of *Drosophila:* Is protein involved in intermediate steps of phototransduction? *Science* **194**: 956–959.

Palka, J. 1990. Neurogenic and anti-neurogenic effects from modifications of the *Notch* locus. *Development* **109**: 167–175.

Pastink, A., Vreeken, C., Schalet, A.P. and Eeken, J.C.J. 1988. DNA sequence analysis of X-ray induced deletions at the white locus of *Drosophila melanogaster. Mutat. Res.* **207**: 23–28.

Pastink, A., Schalet, A.P., Vreeken, C., Paradi, E., and Eeken, J.C. 1987. The nature of radiation-induced mutations at the white locus of *Drosophila melanogaster. Mutat. Res.* **177**: 101–115.

Plough, H.H. 1917. The effect of temperature on crossingover in *Drosophila. J. Exp. Zool.* **24**: 147–209.

Poulson, D.F. 1940. The effects of certain X-chromosome deficiencies on the embryonic development of *Drosophila melanogaster. J. Exp. Zool.* **83**: 271–325.

——. 1950. Histogenesis, organogenesis and differentiation in the embryo of *Drosophila melanogaster* Meigen. In *The biology of* Drosophila (ed. M. Demerec), Hafner Publishing, New York.

Ready, D.F., Hanson, R.E., and Benzer, S. 1976. Development of the *Drosophila* retina, a neurocrystalline lattice. *Dev. Biol.* **53**: 217–240.

Reinke, R. and Zipursky, S.L. 1988. Cell–cell interaction in the *Drosophila* retina: The bride of sevenless gene is required in photoreceptor cell R8 for R7 cell development. *Cell* **55**: 321–330.

Robertson, H.M., Preston, C.R., Phillis, R.W., Johnson-Schlitz, D.M., Benz, W.K., and Engels, W.R. 1988. A stable genomic source of P-element transposase in *Drosophila melanogaster. Genetics* **118**: 461–470.

Rose, L.S. and Wieschaus, E. 1992. The *Drosophila* cellularization gene nullo produces a blastoderm-specific transcript whose levels respond to the nucleocytoplasmic ratio. *Genes Dev.* **6**: 1255–1268.

Schneuwly, S., Klemenz, R., and Gehring, W.J. 1987. Redesigning the body plan of

*Drosophila* by ectopic expression of the homoeotic gene *Antennapedia. Nature* **325**: 816–818.

Sentry, J.W., Yang, M.M., and Kaiser, K. 1993. Conditional cell ablation in *Drosophila. BioEssays* **15**: 491–493.

Simon, M.A., Bowtell, D.D., Dodson, G.S., Laverty, T.R., and Rubin, G.M. 1991. Ras1 and a putative guanine nucleotide exchange factor perform crucial steps in signaling by the sevenless protein tyrosine kinase. *Cell* **67**: 701–716.

Smith, D., Wohlgemuth, J., Calvi, B.R., Franklin, I., and Gelbart, W.M. 1993. *hobo* enhancer-trapping mutagenesis in *Drosophila* reveals an insertion specificity different from P elements. *Genetics* **135**: 1063–1076.

Sprenger, F., Stevens, L.M., and Nüsslein-Volhard, C. 1989. The *Drosophila* gene *torso* enodes a putative receptor tyrosine kinase. *Nature* **338**: 478–483.

Stern, C. 1968. *Genetic mosaics and other essays.* Harvard University Press, Cambridge, Massachusetts.

Stern, M., Dreber, R., and Ganetzky, B. 1990. Dosage effects of a *Drosophila* sodium channel gene on behavior and axonal excitability. *Genetics* **124**: 133–143.

Stewart, B. and Merriam, J.R. 1973. Segmental aneuploidy of the *X* chromosome. *Drosophila Inf. Service* **50**: 167–170.

Struhl, G. 1981. A homoeotic mutation transforming leg to antenna in *Drosophila. Nature* **292**: 635–638.

Struhl, G., Fitzgerald, K., and Greenwald, I. 1993. Intrinsic activity of the Lin-12 and Notch intracellular domains in vivo. *Cell* **74**: 331–345.

Sturtevant, A.H. 1929. The claret mutant type of *Drosophila simulans:* A study of chromosome elimination and of cell lineage. *Z. Wiss. Zool.* **135**: 323–356.

Sturtevant, A.H. and Beadle, G.W. 1936. The relations of inversions in the *X*-chromosome of *Drosophila melanogaster* to crossing over and disjunction. *Genetics* **21**: 554–604.

Suzuki, D.T. , Kaufman, T., Falk, D., and the University of British Columbia *Drosophila* Marching Band. 1976. Conditionally expressed mutations in *Drosophila melanogaster.* In *The genetics and biology of* Drosophila (ed. Ashburner, M. and Novitski, E.), vol. 1a, pp. 207–263. Academic Press, New York.

Sweeney, S.T., Broadie, L., Keane, J., Niemann, H., and O'Kane, C.J. 1995. Targeted expression of tetanus toxin light chain in *Drosophila* specifically eliminates synaptic transmission and causes behavioral defects. *Neuron* **14**: 341–351.

Technau, G.M. 1986. Lineage analysis of transplanted individual cells in embryos of *Drosophila melanogaster.* I. The early days. *Roux's Arch. Dev. Biol.* **195**: 389–398.

Thomas, J.B., Crews, S.T., and Goodman, C.S. 1988. Molecular genetics of the single-minded locus: A gene involved in the development of the *Drosophila* nervous system. *Cell* **52**: 133–141.

Tokunaga, C. and Stern, C. 1965. The developmental autonomy of Extra Sex Combs in *Drosophila melanogaster. Dev. Biol.* **11**: 50–81.

Van Doren, M., Ellis, H.M., and Posakony, J.W. 1991. The *Drosophila* extramacro-chaetae protein antagonizes sequence-specific DNA binding by daughterless/

achaete-scute protein complexes. *Development* **113**: 245–255.

Van Vactor, D., Jr, Krantz, D.E., Reinke, R., and Zipursky, S.L. 1988. Analysis of mutants in chaoptin, a photoreceptor cell-specific glycoprotein in *Drosophila*, reveals its role in cellular morphogenesis. *Cell* **52**: 281–290.

Vincent, J.P., Girdham, C.H., and O'Farrell, P.H. 1994. A cell-autonomous, ubiquitous marker for the analysis of *Drosophila* genetic mosaics. *Dev. Biol.* **164**: 328–331.

Walker, R.A., Salmon, E.D., and Endow, S.A. 1990. The *Drosophila* claret segregation protein is a minus-end directed motor molecule. *Nature* **347**: 780–782.

Welshons, W.J. 1965. Analysis of a gene in *Drosophila*. *Science* **150**: 1122–1129.

Wieschaus, E. 1980. A combined genetic and mosaic approach to the study of oogenesis in *Drosophila*. In *Development and neurobiology of* Drosophila (ed. Siddiqi, O. et al.), pp. 85–94. Plenum Publishing, New York.

Wieschaus, E. and Gehring, W.J. 1976. Clonal analysis of primordial disc cells in the early embryo of *Drosophila melanogaster*. *Dev. Biol.* **50**: 249–263.

Wieschaus, E. and Sweeton, D. 1988. Requirements for X-linked zygotic gene activity during cellularization of early *Drosophila* embryos. *Development* **104**: 483–493.

Wilson, C., Pearson, R.K., Bellen, H.J., O'Kane, C.J., Grossniklaus, U., and Gehring, W.J. 1989. P-element-mediated enhancer detection: an efficient method for isolating and characterizing developmentally regulated genes in *Drosophila*. *Genes Dev.* **3**: 1301–1313.

Wright, T.R. 1970. The genetics of embryogenesis in *Drosophila*. *Adv. Genet.* **15**: 261–395.

Xu, T. and Rubin, G.M. 1993. Analysis of genetic mosaics in developing and adult *Drosophila* tissues. *Development* **117**: 1223–1237.

Zinsmaier, K.E., Eberle, K.K., Buchner, E., Walter, N., and Benzer, S. 1994. Paralysis and early death in cysteine string protein mutants of *Drosophila*. *Science* **263**: 977–980.

# Index

G418, 38
Gain-of-function mutations, 87, 93–94, 96.
    *See also* Hypermorphs;
      Neomorphs
Gal4
  cell ablations. *See* Cell ablations
  enhancer trap, 122
  temperature sensitivity, 123
Genotype synthesis
  doubly mutant embryos, 68
  linking mutations, 64–66
  non-virgin females, 71
  single chromosome manipulations,
    64–66
  three-chromosome manipulations,
    72–73
  two-chromosome manipulations, 66–72
  which sex to use, 71
Gynandromorphs, 72, 104, 106, 108, 112

Haplo-insufficiency, 75, 77
Haplo-lethal loci, 57, 77
Heat shock. *See* Inducible promoters
Hybrid dysgenesis, 27, 40
Hypermorphs, 91–92
  Confluens "allele" of the Notch locus
    (*Co*), 92
  phenotypic severity, 91–92
Hypomorphs, 89–91
  allele doses, 90
  even-skipped, 90
  germ-line transformants, 91
  missense or nonsense mutations, 89
  phenotypic severity, 90
  temperature-sensitive mutations, 90–91
    bithorax allele, $bx^{34e}$, 91
    no-receptor-potential-A (*norpA*)
      locus, 90
    sodium channel gene *para* (paralytic),
      91, 98
    Toll maternal-effect locus, 90

In situ hybridization, 6, 44, 62
Inducible promoters, 100–102
  FLP-FRP system, 101–102, 120
  heat shock, 100–102, 120–121
Inversions, 4, 9
  *In(1)dl-49*, 107
  *In(1)sc⁴*, 9
  *In(1)wᵛᶜ*, 10, 107
  *In(2LR)O, Cy dpˡᵛ¹ pr cn²*, 13

pericentric, 84–85

*lacZ*, 38–39, 68, 122
Legs, extra-sex-combs (*esc*) mutation, 117
Lindsley and Zimm, 6, 53, 55
Loss-of-function mutations, 87, 93–94, 96

Mapping mutations
  deletion mapping, 55
  duplication mapping, 55
  in situ hybridization, 62
  linkage analysis, 41, 47–48
  meiotic mapping, 51–53
  molecular mapping, 53
  P-element insertions, 49
  recessive, 49
  recombination analysis, 47
  synthesis of deletions and duplications,
    56
  using stock strains *T(Y;A)*s, 56–61
Marker mutations, 5
  consistency of expression, 6–7
  dominant
    Antennapedia (*Hu*), 13, 92, 94
    Bar (*B*), 13, 15
    Bar of Stone (*Bˢ*), 10, 56, 83
    Beaded-Serrate (*Bdˢ*), 13
    Curly (*Cy*), 9, 13, 15, 71–72
    "Curly of Oster" (*CyO*), 9, 13
    Dichaete (*D³*), 13
    Henna (*Hnᵖ*), 13
    Scutoid (*Sco*), 9, 14–15
    Serrate (*Ser*), 13, 31, 43
    Stubble (*Sb*), 13, 31, 39, 43
    Tubby (*Tb*), 13
    Ultrabithorax (*Ubx*), 13, 40, 71–72
  interactions between, 7
  recessive
    bithorax (*bx³⁴ᵉ*), 13
    canoe (*cno*), 42
    cinnabar (*cn*), 13
    cubitus interruptus (*ci*), 9, 48
    dumpy (*dp*), 13
    ebony (*e*), 13
    eyeless (*ey*), 9, 48, 58
    garnet (*g⁴*), 13
    hairy (*h*), 10
    lozenge (*lzˢᵖ*), 13, 33
    naked cuticle (*nkd*), 28, 31
    notchoid (*nd*), 14–15
    pink peach (*pᵖ*), 13

# The Development of *Drosophila melanogaster*

Edited by Michael Bate, *University of Cambridge;* Alfonso Martinez Arias, *University of Cambridge*

**--Here's what the reviewers have to say:**

"Bate and Martinez Arias [assembled] a dazzling array of authors to write authoritative essays on topics that range from spermatogenesis and oogenesis to the development of the optic lobe or the alimentary canal. The result is impressive: two massive tomes packed with informative text, illustrations, tables and explanatory diagrams that detail the current understanding of both the postembryonic and embryonic development of the fly....[they have produced] the new version of the bible that will take us into the next millennium."

*— Trends in Genetics*

## CONTENTS

Developmental Genetics of Oogenesis (A. Spradling); Spermatogenesis (M. Fuller); Mitosis and Morphogenesis in the *Drosophila* Embryo: Point and Counterpoint (V. Foe, G. Odell, B. Edgar); Maternal Control of Anterior Development in the *Drosophila* Embryo (W. Driever); Pole Plasm and the Posterior Group Genes (D. St Johnson); The Terminal System of Axis Determination in the *Drosophila* Embryo (F. Sprenger, C. Nüsslein-Volhard); Maternal Control of Dorsal-Ventral Polarity and Pattern in the Embryo (R. Chasan, K. Anderson); Gastrulation in *Drosophila:* Cellular Mechanisms of Morphogenetic Movements (M. Costa, D. Sweeton, E. Wieschaus); Blastoderm Segmentation (M. Pankratz, H. Jäckle); Development and Patterning of the Larval Epidermis of *Drosophila* (A. Martinez Arias); Development of the *Drosophila* Tracheal System (G. Manning, M. Krasnow); The Terminal Regions of the Body Pattern (G. Jürgens, V. Hartenstein); Imaginal Disc Development (S. Cohen); The Metamorphic Development of the Adult Epidermis (D. Fristrom, J. Fristrom); Hormones and *Drosophila* Development (L. Riddiford); The Alimentary Canal (H. Skaer); The Mesoderm and Its Derivatives (M. Bate); Early Neurogenesis in *Drosophila melanogaster* (J. Campos-Ortega); Embryonic Development of the *Drosophila* Central Nervous System (C. Goodman, C. Doe); The Peripheral Nervous System (Y.N. Jan, L.Y. Jan); Formation of the Adult Nervous System (J. Truman, B. Taylor, T. Awad); Pattern Formation in the *Drosophila* Retina (T. Wolff, D. Ready); Genetic Dissection of Eye Development in *Drosophila* (B. Dickson, E. Hafen); The Development of the Optic Lobe (I. Meinertzhagen, T. Hanson); Epilogue (M. Ashburner)

Atlas of *Drosophila* Development (V. Hartenstein)

Poster: *Drosophila* Third Instar Eye Disc (T. Wolff)

**1993, 1564 pp., illus. (147 in color), indexes**        **ISBN 0-87969-423-8**
**2-volume set, cloth; atlas, paper; poster $295**

# Biology of *Drosophila*

Edited by M. Demerec

"...an essential work of reference for any serious fly lab."     Michael Ashburner, 1988

"...the invaluable handbook and guide for generations of *Drosophila* workers."
Michael Bate and Alfonso Martinez Arias, 1993

"...an indispensable source..."
Peter Lawrence, 1994

*Biology of Drosophila* was first published by John Wiley and Sons in 1950. Until its appearance, no central, synthesized source of biological data on *Drosophila melanogaster* was available, despite the fly's importance to science for three decades. Ten years in the making, it was an immediate success and remained in print for two decades. However, original copies are now very hard to find. This facsimile edition makes available to the fly community once again its most enduring work of reference.

## CONTENTS

**Chapter 1: Normal Spermatogenesis in *Drosophila***
K.W. Cooper
**Chapter 2: The Early Embryology of *Drosophila melanogaster***
B.P. Sonnenblick
**Chapter 3: Histogenesis, Organogenesis, and Differentiation in the Embryo of *Drosophila melanogaster* Meigen**
D.F. Poulson
**Chapter 4: The Postembryonic Development of *Drosophila***
D. Bodenstein
**Chapter 5: External Morphology of the Adult**
G.F. Ferris
**Chapter 6: The Internal Anatomy and Histology of the Imago of *Drosophila melanogaster***
A. Miller
**Chapter 7: Collection and Laboratory Culture**
W.P. Spencer

**1994, 632 pp., illus., indexes**
**Cloth $39**

ISBN 0-87969-441-6